THE BODY MAGNETIC

by

Buryl Payne

Copyright 1988
Fifth Edition
September 1991

ISBN   0-9628569-9-1

Box 6023
Boulder, CO 80306

Dedicated to Ralph Sierra
whose warmth and genius sparked
me to work in this exciting
area of inquiry.

PREFACE

Magnetism - the elusive, mysterious force, which forms events from marriages to galaxies, into patterns and structures. Magnetism curls around the tiniest electrons, yet reaches its tendrils into the vast voids between galactic clusters to guide the paths of stars already dying or those yet to be. In another form, it is personal magnetism which accounts for the charisma of a great leader, or the attractiveness of a lover. Every individual being has their unique magnetic pattern and place in the grander symphony of forces and they may or may not be in harmony, and not always by conscious choice or personal power.

The mysterious human aura seems to be another form of magnetism: a higher order of magnetism which is related to the planet's magnetic aura; itself an ever changing blend of celestial magnetic patterns formed by the Sun's grander plan. Magnetically, we are all in interactive resonance not only with each other, but with the moon, the Sun, and all its planets.

Loves and likes, politics and wars, are cast from the same magnetic molds generated by invisible octaves of magnetic forces. Are we mere magnetic puppets penduluming to and fro as these greater forces come and go? Not something those who believe in free will like to hear. And perhaps not true, at least for those who can and do make the efforts required to pit their puny power in and out of synchrony with the higher forces that hold most tight prisoners.

Yet what is magnetism anyway that it can be so powerful, so important, yet so elusive and mysterious? Is it truly one of nature's indivisible, elemental forces? Is it a key aspect of living organisms as well as a property of all matter as both Einstein and Tesla have proclaimed? Or is it merely a convenient catch-all term applied like plaster to cover the cracks of our ignorance about how this universe works?

This book will explore some of the truths we now think we know, about the nature of magnetism, the possible different types of magnetism, and the unexplainables which have been tossed into the box labeled "magnetism" without careful sorting.

What people have done or observed that is solid and repeatable, and what is useful will be found in this book. Different ideas, devices, techniques—whatever is known as of 1989, is presented here so the reader can make his or her own tests and evaluations. Have fun!

TABLE OF CONTENTS

CHAPTER I

THE HISTORY OF
MAGNETIC HEALING

For thousands of years, people have known of the healing power of magnetism. Iron ore, called magnetite, was ground up, used in food preparation, made into ointments, or rubbed in the hair. In Africa, a mine has been discovered that is over 100,000 years old. This mine was a source of red iron ore known as bloodstone or ocher, and was speculated to have been used for healing and special ceremonies. Although ancient Africans presumably had no means of knowing about the physics of magnetism, nevertheless they knew that these special substances had healing properties. Perhaps it was traded in local markets much as herbs and medicine are sold today.

Africans weren't the only peoples to discover the valuable properties of magnetism. Probably you have seen photographs of Egyptian paintings showing the priest holding a cane over the head of a person. Some of these canes still exist and can be seen in the Egyptian museum in Cairo. They appear to be alternate bands of gold and iron. If the iron bands were magnetic, such wands may have been used to stroke the "aura" around an ailing person. Magnets do have an effect when used in this manner, as you will discover for yourself if you try some of the experiments described in Chapter V.

Australian aborigines traveled hundreds of miles to mine ocher or bloodstone for use in ritual ceremonies and other cultures in other times used it for burial rites, witchcraft rituals, and to daub on pots in which special potions were cooked.

The term "magnetism" entered the Greek language a few hundred years before the birth of Christ. There are two versions of the term's origin. In one version, lodestones were found in Magnesia, an ancient district bordering on Macedonia (a region north of ancient Greece). This place was mentioned by the Greek poet, Euripedes (480-405 B. C.). But Plato, writing after Euripedes (420-347 B.C.) gives credit for finding lodestones to a shepherd named Magnes who lived near Mt. Ida.

According to Plato, a Greek physician named Pliny used these lodestones for bladder symptoms, female problems, and to help heal dangerous wounds.

The next recorded use of magnets was about 200 years later. Galen, another Greek physician found that he could draw out pain from many different kinds of illnesses by applying these natural magnets.

The Chinese also knew about the significance of magnets since ancient times. In the first century they had already made observations that certain tiny organisms would orient to Earth's magnetic field. By the seventh century they had already developed the use of the compass to an incredible degree. They were especially knowledgeable about local variations in Earth's magnetic field and corresponding effects on health and disease. This knowledge was called "feng-shui", or the science and art of winds and waters.

According to Stephen Skinner, author of CHINESE GEOMANCY (Rutledge and Kegan Paul, Boston, 1982) the Compass was used by the Fukein School of feng-shui for analysis and detection of ch'i forces (the Chinese name for life energy). The earliest compasses may have come from a divining practice perhaps akin to what dowsers do today. In the practice of feng-shui, the operator does some kind of dowsing combined with the use of a compass. While this has not made sense to the western mind so far, the discovery of the biofield (see Chapter III) may help to bridge the gap between dowsing, ch'i force, and magnetism. These are not the same, but they appear to be related. The Chinese compass had a number of rings around it (up to 15 as shown in Figure 1) each of which designated something about the distribution of ch'i forces. To use it, the diviner would align one ring with the compass needle, then by sighting on nearby land features, water ways, significant vegetation, etc., would read the data on the other rings, to determine the probable ch'i forces at the points of interest. This information was used to locate the best places for building a house, planting a garden, or engaging in some specific ceremony. It was known that local magnetic variations and ch'i forces (possibly obtained by dowsing) were important for human health; something just being rediscovered today by Westerners. Geomancy has been widely used in Germany and is just becoming established in North America.

Figure 1. Chinese Compass, *circa* 1900.

In nearly every country, it seems, people some-how discovered and rediscovered the healing properties of magnets. A Persian physician who lived around 1000 A.D. wrote about using mag-nets to relieve disorders such as gout or to calm muscle spasms. In Europe in the middle ages, physicians ground lodestone into a fine powder and mixed it with other substances to be taken internally. Mixed with honey, magnetic powder was applied to wounds and other ailments.

Early Chinese medical literature mentions the healing properties of lodestone and today modern Chinese physicians use tiny magnets on acupuncture points and meridians to stimulate energy rebalancing and Ch'i flow. (see Chapter III for a possible means of detecting Ch'i force.)

Magnetism was systematically studied in 1600 by William Gilbert, physician to Queen Elizabeth. He took Earth as the model and considered all smaller magnets as miniature Earths. Gilbert considered magnetism to have a 'living quality' and his book on the nature of magnetism was subtitled: "A New Physiology." All early investigators regarded magnetism as a universal principle of attraction and repulsion which was present in both living and non-living matter. As mechanistic science developed during the next 250 years recognition of the possibility that there was a different type of magnetism associated with living organisms was dropped, but it now appears that this was a mistake, as we shall explain later in this book.

In the next century, another physician, Franz Anton Mesmer (1734-1815) played a major part in the history of magnetic healing in western culture. He found, as had so many of his predecessors, that magnets promote healing. He also observed that healing took place even when no magnets were used if the healer used his own body, usually his hands, as part of the healing process. Mesmer's experiences led him to make two inferences:

1. **That there was a kind of magnetism around the human body which he called: "Animal Magnetism".**
2. **That magnets themselves were conductors for this Animal Magnetism possessed by the healer.**

Mesmer also believed that the planets exerted an influence on humans. His dissertation, written in 1766, to receive his medical degree was called: "Physical-Medical Treatise on the Influence of the Planets". Initially, Mesmer did not know the mechanism, but later he believed it was similar to magnetism and it was given the name "Planetary Magnetism".Some of the modern scientific research which validates Mesmer's inferences will be discussed in Chapters III and IV.

Mesmer was considered a charlatan by some members of the medical community; his work with magnets was discredited, and his ideas about animal and planetary magnetism ignored. However, careful study of his work (see references) shows that he was a sincere researcher years ahead of his time.

Magnets have continued to be used by lay people all over the world because they work—they do help many types of ailments heal. We will carry on the threads of Mesmer's work in later chapters after we discuss in detail the nature of this mysterious force called "magnetism" and relate it to the other forces of nature.

As the technology for manufacturing magnets developed, they were more widely used for experimentation. People kept discovering and rediscovering the power of magnets to heal. For example, at one time so-called "bed magnets" were very popular. These were large magnets which were placed under the mattress to help promote a sound sleep and get rid of aches and pains. For some people they worked and now we have a modern equivalent, the magnetic sleeping system; a magnetic pad, cover and pillow (see

Chapter 6).

When electromagnets were developed, more powerful magnets could be made and in the 1920's and 30's magnetic instruments were made to treat a variety of conditions. Some of these early devices probably worked, whereas others were apparently fraudulent, capitalizing on the public's ignorance of science and the mysteriousness of magnetism.

Magnetic instruments and devices did not come into widespread use because the results were inconclusive, or not repeatable, and no known mechanisms could explain the positive results that did occur.

However research has continued; much is now known of the mechanisms involved in biological effects of magnetic healing and now magnetism is ready to take a major role in the physicians' medicine bag.

CHAPTER II

WHAT IS MAGNETISM?

Thousands of years ago people observed that certain heavy rocks attracted or repelled each other. This mysterious movement was assumed to be due to some unknown, invisible force. Since Greek times it has been called 'magnetism' in the western indo-european languages. However, simply naming something does not explain it, or confer understanding to the listener.

Because magnetism is a noun in our language, we tend to think of it as a thing. We were taught that a noun is either a person, place, or thing. This is a subtle, yet powerful kind of mental programming which is built into our language, making it difficult to understand how the world works. Our language structure does some of our 'thinking' for us and we almost automatically come to think that magnetism is a thing added to a substance, like a coat of paint.

It's important to keep in mind that magnetism, like so many terms in science, is simply a word or label, and has no intrinsic meaning at all. Terms like magnetism are often conveniently used to cover our ignorance.

Because magnetic effects seem unexplainable and are invisible to our ordinary senses, they have been invoked as a kind of catch-all for every phenomenon we don't understand. Long ago Mesmer wrote: "I observe with regret that people flippantly abuse this name: once having become familiar with the word 'magnetism', they flatter themselves that they have the idea of the thing, whereas they merely have the idea of a word." (Mesmer/Bloch, p. 110) This is as true today as it was 200 years ago in Mesmer's time.

When iron filings were placed around a magnetized iron bar, they lined up in ordered patterns. These observations led people to believe that the space around a bar magnet had, or contained, some thing, which eventually came to be called the magnetic 'field'. At first considered an imaginary construct, a magnetic field has eventually come to be considered a real thing in its own right, perhaps again illustrating the power of words to crystallize thinking and distort understanding.

We can understand magnetism better if we

place it in context with the other forces of physics*. About 100 years before Mesmer did his work, Newton formulated his laws of motion and gave a mathematical expression to the force known as gravity which was believed to exist between all material bodies on the Earth and in the universe. Gravity was considered to be the fundamental force. It has never been satisfactorily explained—only described.

Magnetism was considered to be a special force operating only between pieces of magnetized iron. At first it was called 'iron magnetism' and eventually just 'magnetism'. Mesmer also believed that there was another force around the human body which was similar to iron magnetism, but different from it. This was later called 'animal magnetism' and will be discussed in the next chapter.

Electricity was another force just beginning to be understood in Mesmer's time, although like magnetism, it had been known since Greek times. Luigi Galvani (1737-1799) who did the famous frog's leg experiments showing that electricity was fundamental for living organisms , was born

---

* Force is the name given to that which moves material objects.

shortly after Mesmer. It was 1800 before the electric battery was developed; just a few years after Mesmer completed his work.

In addition to ordinary iron magnetism two other types of magnetism have been discovered. Some materials are attracted to either pole of a magnet and other materials are repelled by either pole of a magnet. These materials are said to be paramagnetic and diamagnetic, respectively. Most substances are weakly paramagnetic and are attracted by both poles of a magnet. For most materials this is a very weak effect. Iron (in its unmagnetized state) is the most common exception. It is strongly attracted by a magnet and is called "ferromagnetic". Ferromagnetic substances can easily become magnetized to form permanent magnets.

The next step towards understanding the nature of magnetism was made in 1819 by Hans Oersted, a Danish scientist. People had suspected that there was a connection between electricity and magnetism, but no one had so far been able to find it. There were even prizes offered for discovery of this connection.

After a number of experiments, Oersted discovered that when a compass was placed near a wire carrying a current, the compass would deviate from magnetic north. Curious about how large this effect actually is, I decided to repeat Oersted's experiment. To do this, I connected a car tail light to a car battery and placed one of the wires leading to the light directly over the face of a pocket compass. If both wires are used the effect will cancel out. When the light was switched off and on I could just barely see the compass needle wiggle. Had I not been looking for an effect I could easily have missed it. The compass needle moves at right angles to the direction of the current flow. In Oersted's time, it was considered "unreasonable" that a force could be at right angles to the source or cause. The only types of force known were gravitic and electric, and they either pulled or pushed. Oersted's contemporaries reacted violently to his demonstrations. Fortunately Oersted persisted in his experiments and eventually discovered that the force was in the form of circles around the current carrying wire.

Since a compass needle is made of magnetized iron, it was assumed (in 1820) that the force observed around a wire was the same as the force previously observed between lodestones. It was assumed that 'iron magnetism' was the same as electrically created magnetism. Although this assumption is now being questioned, Oersted's discovery opens up many new areas of investigation. Around this period, and especially after Oersted's fundamental discovery, the science of physics and chemistry developed rapidly. Some genius found that by making coils of wires the magnetic force could be greatly concentrated within the center of the coil.

Each individual section of a single coil contributes a bit of magnetic force to the center, whereas outside the coil each section's contribution is dispersed in a larger space. It is the form of the wire which accentuates the magnetic forces; but they are present to a tiny degree around each segment of wire when an electrical current is flowing. A coil of wire is a marvelous and extremely simple invention.

The invention of the coil quickly led to many other developments. Transformers, or coils within coils, were another remarkable invention which allowed voltage and currents to be transformed back and forth. Radio waves, or the propagation of a magnetic force from one coil to another across space, were discovered. The observation that electricity could be made to flow in wires led to the notion that tiny particles of electric charge moved within the wire. This was confirmed and the electric charge of a particle called the "electron" was measured. All types of experiments were conducted and many attempts were made to construct meaningful theories. These were the days of the "ether" concepts; a mysterious, elusive substance which supposedly pervaded all space and time, and in various forms and concentrations, gave rise to electric and magnetic forces or allowed them to exist in so-called "empty space".

The experiments of this era were united by the brilliant work of James Clerk Maxwell (1831-1879). He developed elegant mathematical equations connecting light, radio waves, electricity, and magnetism. His theories stand firm even today and his lucid work shines like a supernova among the ordinary geniuses of science, even after 100 years of rapid progress.

Table 1 summarizes the forces known around the time of Maxwell. Because of experimental observations and Maxwell's unifying equations, it was believed that all so-called magnetic phenomenon arose from forces between electrical charges which are in motion. That is, moving electrical charges exert forces on one another over and above purely 'electrical or electrostatic forces'. How magnetic forces could arise just from the motions of electrons was puzzling, but because Maxwell's equations worked so well, it was generally accepted without further question. Hence, although the forces are listed separately in the table, electric and magnetic forces are interconnected.

Physicists would like to connect gravity with electricity and magnetism in some similar elegant way, but so far no connection has been found, although the author's discovery of a new force and postulate of its generality may provide a missing link (See chapter III).

TABLE 1

THE FORCES OF THE UNIVERSE (*circa* 1900)

FORCE	LEVEL OF OPERATION	EFFECTS
Gravitic	Operates between all matter.	Pulls matter together.
Electric	Only manifests between charged particles.	Pushes or pulls.
Magnetic	Manifests when charged particles are in motion.	Pushes or pulls at right angles to the direction of motion. Only sensed by other charged particles. Causes charged particles to move in circles, spirals, or helixes.

Electric and magnetic forces are now considered to be aspects of one force called electromagnetic, however for reasons which will become apparent later, the author has chosen to keep them distinct. In addition there are two nuclear forces called 'strong' and 'weak' which hold nuclear particles together in the center of the atom. These forces will not be discussed in this book.

Note that the forces in Table 1 are placed in order of increasing complexity. Gravitational forces exist between all particles, moving or stationary. Gravitational forces only pull. This, then, is the simplest, most fundamental or universal force. If only gravity operated in the universe, everything would have clumped together long ago in one big ball. Some theoreticians claim that this happened and then the ball blew apart.

Electric forces, however, bring another level of structure into the picture. Electric forces either pull or push. Although they only appear between some types of particles, those types of particles, called charged, are very common. The conductivity of space within the solar system, for example, is about the same as copper. Negatively charged electrons and positively charged protons, and other charged and uncharged particles are whizzing about everywhere. Electric forces produce more complex forms of matter, but even so, given a very long time, if only electric and gravitic forces were operating, all the positive and negative charges would eventually find each other and cancel out, leaving only the weaker force of gravity to operate and clump everything together.

Magnetic forces bring in another level of complexity because they only appear when charged particles are moving (or so it was believed around 1900), and they push or pull at right angles to the direction of motion of charged particles.

Magnetic forces, acting on moving charged particles, will shape their paths into curved, spiral or helical form. In a cyclotron, magnetic fields force charged particles to take a circular path.

In general, if oppositely charged particles are moving near one another, under some conditions they will form orbits or move in other complicated patterns because of magnetic forces, rather than just simply bang together, their charges annihilating with a flash of light. Most of the time, however, they would eventually find their counterparts, cancel their charges, or form atoms with no net electrical charge, and gravity would again become dominant drawing everything together into one big ball.

That hasn't happened. The universe is even more complicated than the physicists of the early 1900's knew. We may have to add another force or two to Table 1.

In 1895 the British physicist, Ernst Rutherford (1871-1937) discovered that an atom was mostly empty space composed of a tiny nucleus surrounded by orbiting electrons. Initially it was believed that electrons circulating around a nucleus would act like electrons moving in wires to create a magnetic field. Since there were many electrons orbiting around most atomic nuclei, magnetic fields would be expected around every atom. Since such fields aren't observed, except in the case of iron and a couple of other metals, it was assumed that the magnetic fields cancelled each other out. This initial view was not correct.

In the early 1900's more sensitive instruments were developed and physicists discovered more about that fundamental particle, the electron, as well as other particles which make up atomic nuclei. Since atomic nuclei appeared to be made up of positively charged particles or protons, and neutral particles called neutrons, it was postulated that some extra force was present which was holding the protons together against the electric force which would otherwise drive them apart. This came to be called the 'strong nuclear force'. Another force, called the 'weak nuclear force' was also postulated to exist. Neither of these forces will be discussed in this book. They only operate within the nucleus or on that scale of magnitude.

It was discovered in the early 1900's that electrons and some other sub-atomic particles interacted directly with magnetic fields. In the 1930's Paul Dirac, a physicist working on the implications of the quantum theory, found it desirable, (to make the equations work out), to postulate that electrons and other particles were in some sense spinning, although this notion of spin differs from the macroscopic notion of spin. One difference was that the spin of an elementary particle was considered to be quantized, or to be present in discrete steps. This property of quantized spin was found by experiment to interact with magnetic fields. Electrons were sent thru slits and past magnets. Depending on their spins, they ended up in different places. This could be measured.

Many elementary particles have the property called spin and therefore show interaction with magnetic fields. Even light waves and neutrinos, the tiniest known particles, are observed to interact with magnetic fields, though they aren't electrically charged in the way that electrons and protons are.

It is now believed that it is the electron's spin on its own axis that creates the force called a magnetic field, not the orbiting of electrons around the atomic nucleus.

When spin was introduced into physics it clarified the puzzle of iron magnetism. Formerly it was thought that electrons, as they circulated around an atomic nucleus, would create magnetic fields, since moving electrons in a wire produced a magnetic field. Such fields were not observed around atoms, except for iron and a few other elements. But the notion of spin clarified that. It is now believed and experimentally verified, that the spins of individual electrons in most atoms cancel out, but in iron there is an extra electron with an unpaired spin, which results in a minute amount of magnetism. While this happens in the case of other atoms, iron, in its common metallic form, also happens to be organized in such a way that many of the atoms are aligned. This crystalline-like structure brings the minute amount of magnetism of each atom into coherence so that it is macroscopically observed. The little chunks of organized iron atoms are called 'domains' and were first observed by Francis Bitter about 1940 (see references) by placing fine iron powder on a bar magnet.

Some physicists maintain that the magnetic field generated by a current in a wire is due solely to the motion of the electrons, not their spin. One writer claims that some electron spins align when they are in motion and this spin alignment accounts for the observed magnetic field. Perhaps a different picture of the nature of an electron will be helpful. Instead of considering an electron as if it were a spinning little ball, consider it more like a very fine fluid cloud which is rotating. Under the action of an applied voltage, i.e. from a battery, the electron clouds flow down hill, so to speak, from the negative to the positive, streaming out as they move, lengthening in the direction of movement. The electron fluid is not confined to the wire, but only guided by it. The fluid like distortion of space-time is present all around the wire. Normally, these electron clouds are spinning randomly in all directions. When these spinning clouds are forced to move along the wire, they bump into the clouds of other cloud-particles such as the atomic nuclei and electrons which are bound to the nuclei and not free to move. These interactions set the free moving, randomly spinning electron clouds to being jiggled and jostled. They are not free to travel in straight lines and as a result they precess, meaning they wobble about their original axis of individual spins. It becomes a kind of jumbled mess, with trillions of electrons moving along, but on the average a loose helical spin field or torque is set up in the space around the wire and at right angles to it. Any charged particle in the vicinity of the wire is swept along in this jumbled, spinning force called a magnetic field.

While this is strictly the author's own imaginary model, a similar model has been invoked by Paul Dirac and others to explain the nature of the electromagnetic field and to account for the magnetic field of the neutron, which is a neutral particle and therefore shouldn't have any magnetic field. In this model, physicists invoke the idea of virtual particles—which come into existence and disappear in fractions of a microsecond. These virtual particles surround ordinary particles like a cloud. Around electrons, supposedly, are clouds of virtual photons, which spin and which are exchanged with other electrons and protons to account for what we perceive as physical forces.

According to Dirac, a neutron possesses intrinsic spin, which means that as it rotates it drags around clouds of virtual charged particles, setting up miniscule electric currents. These currents produce a magnetic field which can be measured in the laboratory.

Therefore, it seems that every particle, not just charged particles, have associated magnetic fields. Neutrinos, neutrons, photons, protons, electrons, etc. also all have the property called spin. It may be possible to replace the term magnetism by the term spin. The next chapter will describe a novel experiment which apparently shows the presence of spin around living organisms, but first let us conclude and summarize the results of this chapter on the nature of magnetism.

Can spin forces account for all the varieties and manifestations of magnetism that we have observed? Perhaps... and perhaps not. Therefore it seems useful to keep, for a while at least, distinctions between different types of magnetism. Table 2 indicates some different possible types of magnetism. Note that these may not be different types, but just manifestations at different structural or scale levels. Material in later chapters expands on the different types and may help to clarify the relationships between them.

TABLE 2

Types of Magnetism	Structural Level
SPIN	Present around all elementary particles. Show interaction with magnetic fields.
IRON	Present in iron and some other metals under certain conditions. Apparently manifests from spin fields that normally cancel each other out in most materials, but not in iron.
ELECTRO-	Manifests when charged particles move together in an organized manner.
ANIMAL	A special type of spin force present around living organisms which interacts with other types of magnetism (see Chapter III).
PLANETARY	Known to be present around Earth and possibly planets (see Chapter IV). Origin unknown.
STELLAR	Present around stars. Origin unknown.

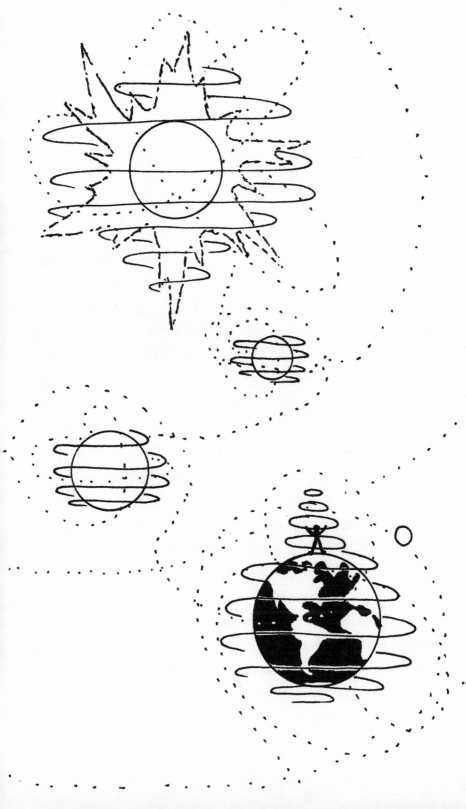

CHAPTER III

DISCOVERY OF THE BIOFIELD— A DIFFERENT TYPE OF MAGNETISM?

Prana, ch´i, orgone, life force, aura, or animal magnetism are some of the terms used to describe a biological energy field (biofield) assumed to exist around living organisms. Prana is an ancient term used by yogis to describe energy taken in by breathing to charge the body. The Chinese use the term ch´i or Ki to describe the energy which circulates along acupuncture meridians and provides the essential life force for the body. In the 1940's Wilhelm Reich built what he called orgone accumulators which collected an energy from space. Orgone was considered to be the vital energy of all living organisms and could be supplied to people who were ill by Reich's accumulators. It's easy enough to build an accumulator, and I made several, but didn't find the results consistent and objectively measurable. Reich's devices and discoveries stimulated a lot of research which is continuing today. There are two journals devoted to Reich's work and a few devices can be purchased from researchers.

Psychics who claim to see the human aura have always tantalized researchers to detect it with the latest and most sensitive instruments. However measurements made with sensitive ultraviolet light detectors, electrostatic or radio wave detectors have found nothing except the typical infrared or heat radiation given off by any warm body, living or non-living.

About twenty years ago a Soviet researcher found that when the skin was charged with high voltage, high frequency electricity, exposed photographic plates would show different colored patterns for different people. The Kirlian effect, as it has been called, after its discoverer, has been widely investigated. Some scientists believe it can be completely explained by traditional electromagnetic effects, while others show evidence supporting the hypothesis that when humans experience different emotions, their Kirlian photographs change. My own observations led me to conclude that there is a genuine effect, but it interacts with the applied electricity and it is not possible to quantify the results.

On a cool, dry day the body can pick up electric

charge, especially if synthetic clothing is worn, and this charge will spark to a metal surface as it is touched, or to another person, if that person has less charge. This comes and goes with the weather; the body does not generate an electric charge which can be detected beyond the skin.

There are small electric currents and voltages generated within the body which can be measured by placing electrodes directly on the skin or placing probes within the brain or heart. Brain waves are only about 10 millionths of a volt and the largest muscle electrical signal is generated by the heart—one quarter of one thousandth of a volt. Other muscles produce voltages of only a few millionths of a volt.

Some people have written that the body has a magnetic aura. Although this has a tiny bit of truth, it is misleading and confusing. While it's correct that any moving electric charge generates a magnetic field, such fields are only a fraction of the strength of the electric fields. In order to make magnetic fields apparent, coils of wire with hundreds of turns must be used. And the current must flow in only one way. Blood flows out and back and has no net electrical charge, so it doesn't generate any external field, although a very small magnetic field is generated when nerve impulses propagate as they move in only one direction. To detect the tiny <u>electrical</u> signal produced by the heart muscle requires amplification of about 1,000 times and electrodes must be placed directly on the body. The <u>magnetic</u> field generated by that tiny signal requires another thousand times as much amplification or a million times altogether. In other words, the magnetic field generated by the heart is only about one thousandth of the electric field. No compass would ever show such a small field.

If the body had an appreciable magnetic aura, compasses would not work properly and people would have been forced to rely on the Sun and stars for navigation.

Within the last decade, a very sensitive instrument has been developed which can detect the very small magnetic fields around the heart and brain, where busy neural activity also makes a tiny net magnetic field. The instrument used to detect these fields is called a SQUID, an acronym for superconducting quantum interference device. The SQUID usually is operated in special magnetically shielded rooms. The SQUID itself, in early models, had to be cooled to liquid helium temperatures to reduce internal electrical noise. The measured magnetic fields from the head and heart are less than one millionth of a gauss (See Chapter V for definition of a gauss). While data from the SQUID is now providing information, to say that the body has a magnetic aura is like saying the body has a gravitational aura. We don't walk around attracting objects to our bodies such as paper clips and rusty nails, by our magnetic fields. However, just because people don't have any appreciable magnetic field, does not mean that they are not affected by small magnetic fields as we shall see in succeeding chapters.

There is another type of field around the body which is not electric nor magnetic and is very much larger than either of them. It is indirectly related to magnetism, and lacking a suitable term, people have often chosen to use the term 'magnetic' to describe it. Mesmer apparently was one of the first people to connect this field with magnetism.

Mesmer believed there was a fluid-like energy around the human body which was highly charged in healthy people, and weak or nearly absent in ill people. He recognized that this field of energy was somehow related to magnetism, and he thought that magnets could conduct it. He called this field "Animal Magnetism" to differentiate it from ordinary iron magnetism. He found that he could produce 'magnetic-like' effects in his patients by stroking the space around them with magnets or his hands. His formulation was similar to what Reich later called orgone energy.

In 1978, the author discovered a simple device which can detect and measure an energy field around the body which may be what Mesmer called animal magnetism. This field shows up as a spin or rotational force on a frame which is suspended over a person's head. Figure 2 shows one form of the device used for this purpose. Although a pyramid frame was initially used, the force field has no connection with so-called pyramid energy. The author was investigating the possible existence of pyramid energy when this other energy effect was accidently discovered.

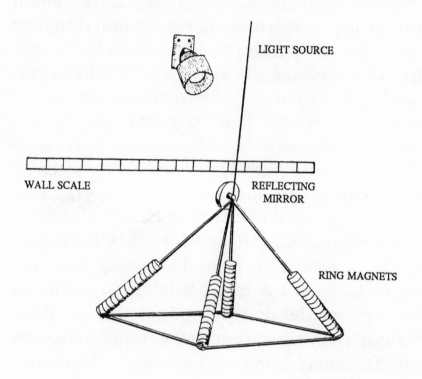

Figure 2. The Biofield Meter

The frame can be of any material; wood, plastic, or metal, and any shape. It is suspended by a nylon filament (fishing line leader). No components are critical. When a person sits under a hanging frame, it will rotate a few degrees. To measure the degree of rotation, a mirror is glued on the nylon filament. A wall mounted spotlight will produce a reflected spot on an adjacent wall where a scale serves to provide accurate measurement of movement of the spot. A lady's compact mirror which slightly focuses the spot of light works better than a flat mirror. In the apparatus shown in Figure 2, ring magnets were placed such that their North poles point towards the apex.

Figure 3 shows a different version of the device which uses a hanging scale. Other versions of the device have included a spiral helix fashioned from quarter inch copper tubing, three sided pyramidal forms, large rings, and pyramids hanging inside a bottle (Figure 4).

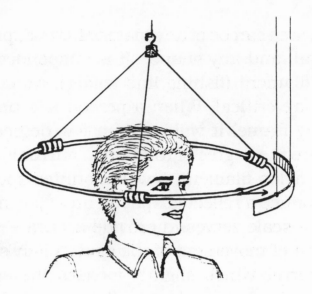

Figures 3   Ring Model Biofield Meter.

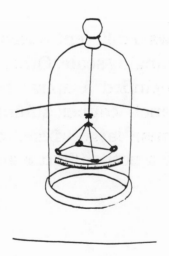

Figure 4.   Original Bell Jar Biofield Meter

Devices have been made and tested with more, less, or no magnets. In general, the more magnets the more movement, but **Biofield Meters still rotate even when there are no magnets on them.** The instruments are stable, and rarely move when no one is near them. Over one thousand observations have been made.

Instruments suspended in bottles demonstrate that air currents and thermal currents could not be involved in their movement. Units placed in bottles or glass cases are caused to move by placing one's hands at the sides of the case. Electrical shielding or electrical grounding of the operator made no difference, however soft iron wrapped around a bottle stopped the effect.

To test whether heat could be producing rotation of the larger frames, several observations were made using a hundred watt light bulb, a lighted candle, and a heat pack. **No movement of the frames was observed when these heat sources were   placed inside the frames.** To insure that air currents produced by breathing were not affecting the movement, the breath was held as long as possible in a number of tests. The

Biofield meter always moved within five to fifteen seconds, so that factor too can be ruled out. Besides the many observations made with units in sealed glass jars have repeatedly demonstrated that movement takes place when no air currents and only minimal heat transfer could be present. Devices in bottles have been observed to move at distances up to 12 feet from the observer during times of large magnetic storms.

Since the body's intrinsic magnetic field measured in shielded rooms is about one billionth of a gauss (see Chapter V for definition of gauss), this biofield could not be an ordinary magnetic field. The author has simply called it the Biofield, a contraction of biological energy field. Tesla, a contemporary of Edison and inventor of the alternating current motor and many other instruments, was reported to have spoken about a 'higher octave' of magnetism which had not been recognized by traditional science.

Whatever we choose to call it; the aura, animal magnetism, orgone energy, prana, spin force, ch´i, or the biofield, this energy is quite large; over

100 million times as large as the body's magnetic field!

If it were magnetic the biofield would be equivalent to several hundred gauss.

Well, then, what is the biofield? It appears to be a genuine new force in science. It manifests as a physical force clearly observed on all types of ordinary physical matter. As of this time (1989) it appears to be a force which produces movement at right angles around the human body. It does not push or pull like gravity or electrostatic forces. It appears to be in the form of a circle of spiral around the body. **The origin of the force is not electrical, magnetic, heat, or gravitational.** It is much too large to be produced by these forces. It needs a name. The author has chosen to call it simply the biofield, and to call the instruments which serve to detect it, biofield meters. Descriptive equations will follow upon the development of additional and more refined instrumentation and further experimentation. New discoveries can probably be made by any reader of this book willing to construct a biofield meter and make careful observations.

After several months of observations it was discovered that the amount of the initial rotational deflection of the Biofield meter varied in association with the geomagnetic field (see Chapter IV for explanation of geomagnetic activity.) Figures 5 and 6 show deflections of the meter over a 40 day period (daily measurements) and a 3 day period (measurements made at 3 hour intervals). The dashed line shows measurements made with the Biofield meter and the solid line shows data on Earth's magnetic activity provided by the National Bureau of Standards in Boulder, Colorado. At times of higher geomagnetic activity, the biofield also showed higher activity. (See Chapter IV for a more detailed explanation of the geomagnetic index.)

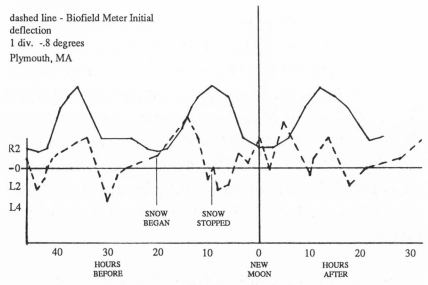

Figure 5. Geomagnetic Data and Biofield Meter deflections before, during, and after The New Moon, Feb. 13, 1983 - Four Day Period.

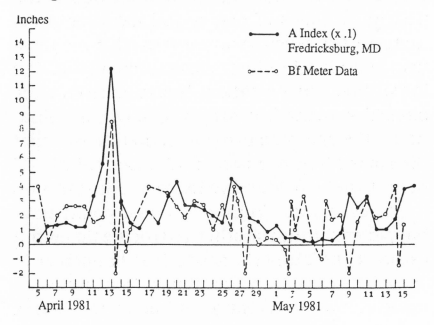

Figure 6. Geomagnetic Index (A) and Biofield Meter Deflections One inch = .8 degrees. A index is divided by 10 - Forty Day Period.

The second figure shows a similar relationship for the three hour variations. There is a clear connection between the two measures, although it's not appropriate to do statistical correlations since there is definitely a component to the biofield data which varies with the emotional state or vitality of the person. When one meditates or is ill, their biofield is of lesser amplitude. When one is excited, either angry or happy, their field is larger.

Usually the direction of the initial rotation of the frame is to the right as seen from within the frame, or clockwise as seen from above the person. At times of new or full moon or when there are large disturbances in Earth's magnetic field the biofield often shows a change in the initial direction of rotation. Measurements of the biofield were made nearly every day. Examination of the data for a two year period showed that 85% of the time of a new or full moon (within 36 hours), the biofield showed a reversal in direction for a few hours. Such a reversal could have happened during the other 15% of the times but escaped the author's notice if it happened to occur between observation times. Measurements made over a seven year period on various forms of biofield meters showed consistent connections between their movements and solar/geomagnetic activity. This was so, even for those forms of the biofield meters which did not have magnets placed on them. It seems that the geomagnetic activity is the largest component of biofield activity.

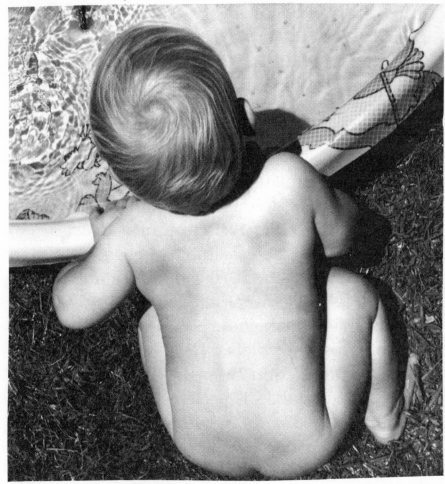

Hair Pattern Swirls—Evidence for a Biofield?

The author detected biofields around a water-melon, a grapefruit, and several plants. Presumably all living organisms have such fields. A literature search uncovered reference to an article by Dr. Charles Ross published in the 1922 medical journal Lancet. He described an instrument which was set in motion by the proximity of the human body or by vision. In recent years a German scientist, W. Peschka, appears to have discovered a similar effect. These men did not obtain numerical data on the amplitude of the field or notice its connection with the geomagnetic field.

Dr. Frank Brown was a pioneer in the study of interactions between magnetism and living organisms. He visited the author's laboratory in 1983 and observed the biofield meter with great interest. Among the 50 reprints of scientific papers he left as a gift were several studies on bean seeds, magnetism, and spin. He found that when bean seeds were placed near one another there was an interaction between them which could not be explained. The effect was observed by carefully measuring the amount of water which the beans absorbed.

Dr. Brown thought the interaction was due to magnetism because it was still present when electrostatic shielding was in place, but nearly disappeared when magnetic shielding was used. Although he believed the bean seeds had a magnetic field, he did not have the instrumentation to measure it. In fact, even if a magnetic field around a bean seed could be detected by an ultra-sensitive SQUID apparatus, it would probably be far too small to account for the observed effects. It seems more likely that the interaction between the bean seeds was due to the presence of a biofield or spin force. The biofield around living organisms appears to be thousands of times larger than the magnetic field.

That the biofield was involved is supported by Dr. Brown's observation of a connection between rotation and bean seed interaction. He found that the beans interacted more strongly when they were rotated counterclockwise than when they were rotated clockwise.

In another series of experiments he placed rotating magnets near the bean seeds and observed an interaction with the bean seeds. Brown and his associates also found interactions between geomagnetic activity and rotation of worms and other small life forms.

Brown also reported on the search of R.I. Jones, who reported in 1960 that plant growth could be altered by uniform daily rotation. Clockwise rotation depressed growth. No one has been able to explain Jones' findings, but the presence of a spin force around all plants might be a factor.

Taken together, the findings of Brown, Jones, the author, and other researchers all point to connections between living organisms, spin, and geomagnetic activity. **All living organisms seem to be in resonance with Earth's dynamic magnetic aura**. And, as will be shown in the next chapter, Earth's magnetic field is in turn a function of solar activity and the positions of the Moon, and at least some of the planets.

RESEARCH POSSIBILITIES FOR THE BIOFIELD

Since the spin force has been observed around plants, a grapefruit and a watermelon, presumably it is present around all living things. Therefore it would be possible to suspend a biofield meter around a plant and continuously monitor the rotation. If no magnets were used on the biofield meter, there should be no magnetic perturbations and the movement of the meter might accurately reflect the geomagnetic activity, whereas in the case of human subjects, emotional states and vitality factors are more variable. Such an apparatus could be set up in a draft free environment, a Faraday cage, or a magnetically shielded room.*

To make measurements of a human's field in a magnetically shielded room would be an excellent way to determine how much of the biofield was generated by the human and how much induced by geomagnetic activity.

---

*The reader can easily make a biofield meter using simple household materials such as copper tubing, wood, or plastic rings for the frame; string or nylon fishing line for suspension, etc. Materials aren't critical. Apparently the biofield acts on all matter. The use of magnets on the frame is optional.

A standardized biofield meter is now available from Dowling Magnetics Corporatioon in Sonoma, California (see Sources Chapter).

Biofield instruments in bottles have been taken to the pyramids of Egypt, the Grand Canyon, the ruins of Palenque, the mountains and the seashore. Inside the great pyramid, there was no detectable biofield. On top of the pyramid, movement was as usual. Differences were observed at other locations as well. In general the amplitude of initial rotation is less near the coast. Since the geomagnetic field strength varies minute by minute, thorough observations on place differences need to be made using standard instruments and simultaneous observation. Some careful experimental procedures would be necessary to make such tests.

Some other questions for research are:
Does the strength of the biofield vary with altitude? Would it diminish in deep mines? Can it be detected in a steady, high flying aircraft? How much mass can actually be caused to move by this force? The heaviest device the author used weighed about 9 pounds. However this weight was not being lifted, only rotated, so very little physical force was actually required.

How do the biofields of individuals interact or combine? If a large ring is suspended over one person and a measurement made, then will two people crowded under the ring increase the amplitude of initial rotation by a factor of two?

Suppose a biofield meter is hung in the center of an empty room and people quietly come in and stand around it. If the mirror system is used, a spot of light can be reflected from the mirror on the biofield meter to a distant wall providing a very sensitive indicator of rotation. If people surround the instrument, moving slowly, towards it, how close do they have to come before it rotates? Or will it rotate at all? How many people will be required to observe such a rotation?

How far does this force field extend around the body? How much interaction is there with the force fields of other humans? Of plants? Of animals? Although the field strength can vary from moment to moment, depending on the activity of Earth's magnetic field and on the emotional state of the human at a given moment, if these are held reasonably constant, how rapidly does it diminish? Gravitational, electrostatic, and magnetic forces have been found to diminish with the square of the distance. Does this force follow the same formula? There are so many parameters to uncover! It's as if we were back in the 1800's when electricity and magnetism were first discovered—an experimenter's paradise.

A most important question is: what is the direction of this force? Is it truly a spin force? The formal and informal experiments and observations I made extending over many years suggest that it is a spin force, but that could be disproved by another type of experiment. The devices I built never seemed to move in another manner except rotation, but that may be because less energy is required to spin the rings or frames than move them in any other way. When a 30 ft. long suspension line was used, spinning still occurred—not swinging. The pyramids hung in bottles rotated when hands were placed at the sides. Is there a spin force between one's hands? This is a puzzle . . .

Ralph Stone, founder of Polarity Therapy, has illustrations showing a spin field around the body. One person who meditates reported to me that she experienced a spinning sensation during a meditation. Perhaps there really are whoosh birds after all! If this force were a spin force it would fit with other patterns found in nature. The photograph shows the spiral pattern of the hair which is commonly found on babies. (Does it spiral the other direction in Australia and New Zealand?) Laurence Badgley has found that a spiral vortex field appears around sites of injury on the body, which shows interaction with magnetic fields.

If the force were in a spin form, it would imply that if we could place a small test object in space around a human, that object would start to spin. This experiment could not be done on Earth, but perhaps it could be done in space. If so, the spin force or life force is similar to magnetism, for it, too, is a spin force located in the space around a wire carrying an electric current.

Whereas magnetic forces only act on other magnets, this life force or biofield force apparently acts on all matter. Copper, iron, aluminum, plastic, and wood have been tried, but quantitative comparative measurements have not been made. If a material were found which did not show the effect it would be a very important discovery.

GENERALIZATION OF THE SPIN FORCE

Spin forces are not unique to living systems—they are omnipresent in the universe. Spin or angular momentum is associated with most sub atomic particles such as electrons, protons, neutrons, etc. Apparently every body in the universe spins! Interstellar molecules spin. Stars, planets, satellites, even entire galaxies and clusters of galaxies all are known to spin. One astronomer maintains that the whole universe spins! A German scientist, Dr. D. Ashcoff has invented an instrument known as a spin-tester for the cells of the body. The discovery of the biofield meter shows the existence of a spin force around the human body and other living organisms. Perhaps it is time to assume that spin be taken as a fundamental force in its own right along with gravity, electricity, and magnetism. Spin, connects gravity and magnetism, for it is a more general type of magnetism and at the same time it complements gravity. Spin forces, if they exist around suns and planets, would help to organize solar systems and satellite systems. The existence of spin as a force would account for why the universe has not come together in clumps, for spin forces operate at right angles to gravity forces.

The fastest spinning Pulsar was recently discovered (proof not yet definite) at the core of a supernova which was observed in the Southern Hemisphere two years ago. This fast spinning Pulsar was apparently formed as part of the supernova process and would be expected to start out spinning slowly and gradually increase in spin as more matter was drawn to the center. But it's measured spin rate is almost 2,000 times per second upsetting traditional theories. How this enormous object could spin so rapidly, apparently so soon after birth, is an unsolved mystery. However it does lend additional support to the notion that spin should be considered a fundamental force present around all matter.

Assuming the existence of spin force as a force in its own right also would bring one aspect of aliveness into the equations of physics, something that is long overdue.

Spin forces might be called 'form forces' or 'organizing forces', for they help form complex living organisms, which abound with spirals, helixes, and circles over and over again in myriads of different ways from double helices in DNA and RNA to Whirling Dervishes.

If we consider that spin be taken as a fundamental force along with gravity, electricity and magnetism, Table 1 can be expanded. (Actually the more precise scientific term for spin is 'torque', the product of force multiplied by distance from the center of the body, human, plant, animal, planet or star.)

TABLE 1 (Expanded)

THE FORCES OF THE UNIVERSE

FORCE	LEVEL OF OPERATION	EFFECTS
Gravitic	Operates between all matter.	Pulls matter together.
Electric	Only manifests between charged charged particles.	Pushes or pulls.
Magnetic	Manifests when charged particles move.	Pushes or pulls at right angles to the direction of motion. Only sensed by other charged particles.Causes charged particles to move in circles, spirals, or helixes.
Spin	Present around all bodies - Much larger around living organisms.	Causes all bodies to spin around one another. Counteracts gravity. Produces complex forms or structures

As previously mentioned there are also two other forces now known to exist. Called the strong and weak nuclear forces, they operate within atomic nuclei to help keep nuclear particles from dispersing due to electrical forces.

More research on the biofield is urgently needed and it's impossible for one person to do it, so it is the author's hope that a lot of readers will take up the exciting challenge and enjoy the fun of exploring a whole new field.

CHAPTER IV

PLANETARY MAGNETISM

Astrology was discredited even before Mesmer's time because no physical mechanism except gravity was known which could operate between Earth and the planets, and gravity was far too weak to affect human behavior. Mesmer proposed that astrology be reinstated as a science as he believed there was some force more subtle than gravity which linked us with the planets and he thought that this force was related to magnetism. In his time this force came to be called "planetary magnetism".

Now, with the development of sensitive measuring instruments, data from space probes, and laboratory research of many scientists, we know that Earth, Sun, Moon, and many of the planets are linked together by magnetic forces. All living organisms appear to respond to minute magnetic changes. Health and disease, peace and war, calm and stormy weather, and some volcanic and earthquake activity are often associated with large disturbances in Earth's magnetic field.

Einstein considered the origin of Earth's magnetic field to be one of the most important unsolved problems in physics. It was once believed that Earth's magnetic field was generated by molten iron rotating within the core, but this is now questionable.

The magnetic poles of Earth are not exactly opposite. A line joining them misses Earth's center by 11,000 kilometers. The location of Earth's poles also temporarily changes by several hundred km when there are magnetic storms caused by solar wind particles.

Six to seven thousand years ago Earth's magnetic field was only half as strong as it is today; then it began to increase, reaching a maximum about 1500 years ago, and is slowly decreasing at the present time.

About every 650,000 years, Earth's magnetic field reverses, but this is not a regular cycle and can't be predicted. If this were to happen now it would be calamitous for life on Earth, because Earth's magnetic field shunts aside particles from the Sun, shielding us from their impact. During the time when the magnetic field was zero, solar particles would strike the surface of the Earth unhindered. We would be zapped!

' Earth's magnetic field is a variable as the surface of the sea, with little waves on top of bigger waves, and froth on top of the little waves, with tides that come and go, seasonal changes, and stormy days that churn it's surface as well as tranquil days when it is as smooth as glass.

There is a small daily variation in the GM field which is related to the positions of the Sun and Moon. The Moon has much less effect than the Sun. There are also differences in the magnetic field at different locations, and the entire globe has been magnetically mapped. Geologists use magnetic field changes as one parameter in looking for oil or natural gas deposits.

In addition to theses regular changes, moment to moment changes are constantly occurring. The smallest changes are called micropulsations, which are ripples close in frequency to some brain rhythms. The larger changes are called magnetic storms. These can last for an hour or two or for a couple of days, and like severe weather storms can make life a little more diffcult for humans and their puny activities.

Earth's magnetic field is called the geomagnetic field (GM field), and although invisible to us, could be considered the planet's aura, just as the biofield could be called our personal aura. The GM field penetrates everywhere, passing easily through rocks, water, air, and extending thousands of miles into space. It varies continuously and even though these variations are only a few hundredths of a per cent, they (or something associated with them) are extremely important for all living organisms. When the GM field is active, our personal aura or biofield increases.

The National Bureau of Standards, in Boulder, Colorado, collects magnetic data from observatories all over the world and provides reports to all interested researchers. Figure 7 shows a sample record during the time of a large magnetic disturbance (called a "magnetic storm") and for the day following, when the magnetic variations returned to normal. Although these variations are so small that they will just barely cause a sensitive compass needle to wiggle, they can trigger changes in the human body, in other animals and in plants.

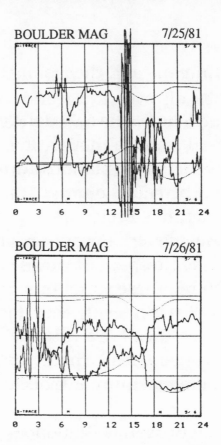

Figure 7. Geomagnetic Field Graphs of
Large Magnetic Storm and Day Following.

Figure 7 shows the horizontal variations (top
line in each block) and vertical variations (bottom
line) in amplitude during a magnetic storm which
occurred about noon on July 25, 1981 and on a
more normal day following the storm. A magnetic
storm can last for minutes, hours, or sometimes
several days. This figure shows the actual raw

data which is continuously recorded at magnetic observatories all over the world. This data is analyzed and a magnetic index is derived from it. This magnetic index, called Ap—the planetary geomagnetic activity, is widely publicized and used (as in Figures 5,6, 9, and 10).

Ap is a number which varies from about 10 to 20 on average days and can increase to over 100 on magnetically stormy days. This number is a rough measure of the heights and wiggles of the raw data as shown in Figure 6.

Magnetic storms sweep over the entire Earth within minutes and can generate enough force to produce large voltages in telephone wires, interfere with radio reception, or cause computers or other delicate equipment to malfunction. Living organisms are more sensitive than electronic equipment and therefore even more susceptible to malfunction at times of GM storms. Gauquelin, a French researcher, reports on a number of studies showing increased accidents, heart attacks, blood disease, and other ailments at times of heightened solar activity. Even the flu has shown increases at times of solar activity. Becker and other researchers found that admission to mental hospitals increased at times of GM storms.

Three physicians at the Crimean Medical Institute in Simferopol, USSR analyzed records of hospitalization of schizophrenic patients for 30 years. They found that the main frequencies of hospitalization of schizophrenia coincided with rhythms of solar activity, and geomagnetic fluctuations. They also report that genetic predisposition for schizophrenia varies with fluctuations of natural magnetic fields at the time of birth.

An English physician found that six major flu epidemics of this century were synchronized with cycles of sunspot activity. Another researcher noted that the flu bugs also altered themselves each solar cycle (except one) so they could bypass the immune system response already built up in people since the last attack. It is not known how solar activity affects living organisms, probably there is both a direct influence by some radio frequencies which do penetrate Earth, such as the 3 gigahertz frequency which interacts with DNA, and indirectly by magnetic field changes produced by solar electrons and protons. Solco Tromp, director of the Biometeorological Research Center in the Netherlands claims, based on studies of 730,000 males, that sunspot cycles are related to blood sedimentation rate and fluctuations in the amount of albumin and gamma globulin. These substances can alter resistance to infection.

Dr. Frank Brown, a biologist who worked at Woods Hole Marine Biological Laboratories, has written about 50 papers on responses of animals and plants to geomagnetic parameters.

It is hard to image how living organisms could be so sensitive to such small field changes, which are on the order of one thousandth of Earth's normal field strength, but it is so. Soviet researchers Gnevyshev and Novikova point out that all sensors in the human organism- -visual, auditory, taste, smell, and tactile, are able to detect energy levels that are comparatively larger than the geomagnetic energy changes by a factor of from 100 to 100,000 times. So whatever the mechanism of geomagnetic detection, it doesn't have to be even as sensitive as our other senses to detect significant changes.

It could also be that the geomagnetic field actually carries information as well as just being a physical impulse. After all, our other senses give us a great deal of information about the external world.

Personal observations by the author on his own behavior and that of others has shown over and over that times of personal upsets occurred at times of GM peaks or solar activity. If you keep a diary you can check for such correlations in your own life by obtaining the weekly data from the National Bureau of Standards, or monthly data from the author (See Chapter XI). Not all GM storms trigger catastrophes or upsets, and people differ in their sensitivity.

For instance while writing the final corrections for this edition one of the largest solar flares of the cycle took place on March 12, 1989 (three planets were in line at that time). The author's landlady had a screaming fit about papers and boxes of files being in one corner of the dining room and so forth. Such behavior by others makes it harder to do creative work. Then 8 days later, just prior to the full moon, at the time of another large solar flare she had another upset, threatening to throw the typewriter out, etc. The author couldn't maintain even temperedness himself under such threats and had to go jump in the ocean- so it goes with us humans.

This is an area for fruitful research; hopefully ways could be found to counteract such events and effects.*

---

* Personal interactions appear to be also partially dependent on what may turn out to be a new type of magnetism or magnetic effect so minute that it still remains far beyond our ability to detect it. For the past ten years the author has been engaged in research on relationships. It now seems clear that love and sex and marriage attractions, and divorce are influenced by planetary effects, probably thru the mechanism of the geomagnetic field and in turn on the biofield. The system investigated by the author is different from that used by astrologers, although it has some similarity in principle, and seems much more accurate. Not only love and sex, but all interpersonal harmony depends on these factors. Employee-employer relations, parent-child relations, or friendships are all affected to a considerable degree by what may prove to be sub-atomic magnetic configurations. (See Sources Chapter for details.)

Humans have very close connections with what happens "out there." For instance, psychic abilities have been found to increase at times of geomagnetic activity (M. Persinger), and people are often more mentally and physically active.

It has often been said that people should sleep with their heads to the North. Consider that the human body is like an antenna. In the case of a TV antenna we rotate it to pick up the most radio energy. In the case of our body, we should rotate it to pick up the least magnetic energy. That way, magnetic disturbances, if there are any, will be less likely to produce biochemical reactions in our bodies or disturb our sleep.

Research is now going on in laboratories in India, China, Europe, and the U.S. to discover how magnetic fields affect the chemistry of the living cell, the nervous system, or the circulatory system. (This will be discussed more fully in Chapter VII.)

Primary variations in the GM field are produced by the Suns' activity and modulated by the position of the Moon. The Sun continuously emits streams of charged particles, mostly electrons and protons, which travel at speeds varying from 400 to 700 meters per second. This stream, called the "solar wind," was discovered about twenty years ago when space probes began monitoring the region outside Earth's atmosphere. Near Earth the solar wind is caused to move in curved paths by Earth's magnetic field. This happens because charged particles experience a force at right angles to their direction of motion in the presence of a magnetic field (See Chapter II).

The Earth's magnetic field is our shield, warding off this radiation. But in the process, Earth's field is disturbed as illustrated in Figures 5, 6 and 7. It literally wiggles and rocks.

When the moving particles constituting the solar wind collide with air atoms high in the ionosphere, light is given off. This is known as the aurora borealis. The weather may be more stormy a day or two later and people more upset as their biofields increase and their body chemistry alters. The Earth's rotation can even alter slightly, producing stress on land masses which could trigger earthquakes or volcanic activity.

The solar wind, rushing by Earth, forms a long wake behind it, rather like the pattern left behind by a boat moving on the surface of the sea. This is called the geomagnetic tail.

When the Moon is new, it is between Earth and Sun and interferes with the solar wind, altering the GM field downstream. When full, the Moon is passing through the GM tail and sometimes produces turbulence which is observed on Earth. It is well known that at times of new and full moon, people become more hyperactive or upset than usual. Observations of the biofield show a reversal of spin direction at such times. Since the solar wind flow changes constantly, the moon's interaction with it also varies and therefore the effect of each new or full moon is always different.

The individual planets also have a direct influence on Earth's magnetic field. Exactly how this can happen is puzzling. Although some of the planets have larger magnetic fields than Earth, others, such as Mercury, Venus, and Mars, have much smaller fields. The classical formula of physics says that the strength of a magnetic field decreases as the square of the distance from the source. But perhaps the magnetic effects between planets are more like tuned radio circuits which can detect very tiny signals by the use of resonant circuits. Amplification may even occur in Earth's upper atmosphere. Amplification of radio signals in the ionosphere by a factor of 1,000 has been found to occur in some circumstances.

As hypothesized in Chapter II, there could be another type of magnetism present around planets which our instruments are not designed to detect. Perhaps a "higher octave of magnetism" as Tesla is reported to have said—whatever that means, or a kind of spin force, analogous to that which seems to exist around living organisms, may be present around celestial bodies and what we see as a magnetic force may be only the faintest remnant or secondary effect of the main force. In order to maintain open ended thinking, planetary magnetism is listed as a separate type in Table 2 of Chapter II.

Stars may have an even higher octave of magnetic force around them, Some stars have enormous magnetic fields. Even the galaxy as a whole appears to have a magnetic field.

Dr. Halton Arp, an astronomer at Mt. Wilson Observatory, has found evidence of a magnetic field associated with the entire galaxy, although it is perhaps 100,000 times weaker than Earth's magnetic field. Astronomers believe that magnetic forces may help to give spiral galaxies their characteristic shape, but there are still puzzles. The author's postulate of the existence of a universal rotational force which operates at the galactic level as well as at the sub-atomic level may help clarify some questions of how galaxies and other celestial organisms form and evolve. Detailed calculations will be required to clarify the hypothesis.

It seems unlikely that the stars or the galactic center or other galaxies could have an effect on Earth's magnetic field and therefore on humans, but an open-minded scientist would not close out this notion without careful analysis of the data. So far only the rather crude measure of GM activity published by NOAA, not the original raw data, has been analyzed by the author and it has been clearly found that planetary positions correlate with changes in this parameter. A German scientist, Theodore Langschiedt, claims to have found evidence for an increase in solar activity associated with Earth transits of the galactic center, so the subject is open for further investigation.

It now (as of 1989) appears that there are two mechanisms by which planetary positions affect Earth's magnetic field:

1) When two or more planets align with the Sun, sunspots and solar flares form and particles spray from them. If Earth is nearby or comes within range in a few days as the sun rotates, there will be a change in the GM activity.

2) When two or more planets align with respect to the Earth there is often a noticeable effect on the GM field. This effect is larger if the planets are closer to Earth, and if the Moon is also in line with those planets, or at 120 degrees with them.

In addition to planetary influences, the Sun has its own rhythms and patterns which also affect the GM field.

Probably each planet has its own unique magnetic 'signature' in Earth's constantly changing magnetic field, only it doesn't show in the crude geomagnetic index unless two or more planets align to bring the influence above the background noise. Perhaps computer analysis of the raw data—the complex wave form that constitutes the ever changing GM field—would show patterns unique to every planet as the moon makes aspects with them. The magnetic storm portrayed in Figure 7ˋ probably was the result of the alignment of Jupiter and Saturn as seen from Earth. They both have much larger magnetic fields than Earth.

Figure 8 shows the geomagnetic activity index for the spring of 1983. The planets Saturn and Pluto were nearly in line that year and every time the moon was either at 120 degrees or in line with them there was a dramatic increase in the geomagnetic activity. In New England, cold and stormy weather accompanied all of the 13 magnetic peaks. For several years, during the spring, when Earth was nearer in its orbit to these slower moving planets, the weather was unusually severe. Most of the storms, cyclones, and tornados during those months coincided with lunar alignments with Saturn and Pluto. The links appear to be magnetic, not gravitic in nature, as changes in the magnetic field of Earth alter high altitude ionospheric winds which in turn affect storminess.

In late April, 1986, when Earth was again near Pluto and there was a full moon which was lining up with Pluto, record low temperatures were observed in 55 American cities. (See Figure 11, pg. 84.) This is a yearly effect, but differs in intensity depending on where the Moon is at the time of the exact opposition, and depending to some extent on positions of some of the other planets, but especially Saturn.

In 1989 Saturn and Pluto were about sixty degrees apart and this appeared to account for some geomagnetic storminess and cold weather every few days during the late spring when the Moon made nearly simultaneous aspects with them. On May 4, Earth passed distant Pluto in its slow moving orbit. From May 3 to May 5 larger than usual solar flares occurred. The Moon was new and at 120 degree angle with Saturn. The geomagnetic field was disturbed and there were severe weather storms around the world. Some of the heaviest snowfall ever to occur so late in the spring was reported from Chicago to Rochester, New York, while torrential floods caused damage in Maine, China, Hong Kong, and other places around the world. Record low temperatures occurred in San Juan, Puerto Rico. A snowstorm in the Soviet Union killed 60,000 sheep and goats and did extensive damage to fruit and cotton crops. Many homes were damaged.

Saturn's position at either conjunction, 60 or 120 degree angles seems to synergistically combine with Pluto to produce more severe weather. The next time when this will occur will be around May 20-21, 1996 when Saturn will be at a 120 degree angle to Pluto. It will probably snow in New England and be unseasonably cold and stormy in many other countries. The effect will be at a maximum around May 20-21, but will be noticeable beginning around March and show up every nine days in association with the Moon's aspects with Saturn and Pluto. This is a world wide phenomenon, but of course, there are local variations. It can't snow or rain everywhere all at once!

However, it is not simply the magnitude or the number of solar flares or GM disturbances that determine the stormy weather; it may be that different solar flares have different qualitative effects. Perhaps the wave forms of the magnetic storms are different in important ways that have not yet been recognized.

While Pluto and Saturn seem to be associated with cold and stormy weather, Jupiter and possibly Venus, have an opposite effect. When Jupiter is nearest Earth, the weather is often unusually warm. In early October, 1987 record high temperatures were recorded on the West Coast. This effect, as well as the Pluto cold effect, happens nearly every year and is quite predictable.   E.K. Bigg, a geophysicist, found that Jupiter's proximity is associated with a calming effect on the geomagnetic field. This does not seem to be so clear and repeatable as the Pluto effect.

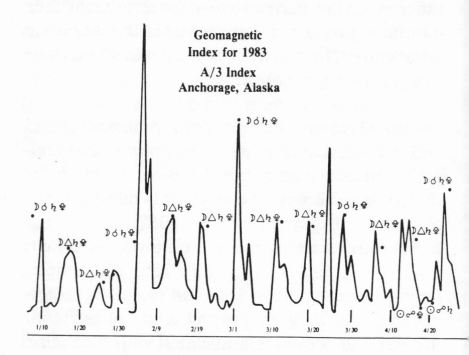

Figure 8. Influence of Saturn and Pluto
on the GM Index

The Sun, of course, has the largest effect on the
GM field and the most influence on human
behavior, putting us to sleep each night and
waking us at dawn. The Sun produces a complex

spectrum of radiations, particles, and magnetic pulses which affect all life on Earth. DNA has been found to resonate at 3 gigahertz, for instance, a very high frequency radiation which, probably by no coincidence, penetrates Earth's atmosphere to reach us. The Sun is so complex and varied in its behavior that it could seriously be considered to be a living being, not just an inert, hot blob, mechanically spinning and burning until it runs down. At least one paper has been written on this hypothesis, and many ancient religions were based on this belief.

The Sun's well known 11 year cycle of activity mixes with planetary cycles forming a complex pattern and humans seem to march in step to this pattern in their general or mass behavior. Dewey and Wheeler found that for 2,500 years the number and severity of international battles have waxed and waned in nearly regular cycles. The author analyzed their data and demonstrated a clear connection between the onset of battles and solar activity. This is illustrated in Figure 9. Only some of the world wide battles are printed above the bars in the figure. On the average international battles start a couple of years before solar activity peaks and less frequently a year or two after sunspot peaks, but never right on the peaks. A geophysicist, Arthur Hundhausen, observed that geomagnetic activity peaked either just before sunspot peaks or just after, so magnetic disturbances again appear to be a key factor in that pathological behavior of humanity—wars.

In 1982 when this chart was first constructed it was predicted by the author that June, 1988 would be a likely time for international battles to increase as six planets were lining up in a unique pattern which had not occurred for 9,240 years. About 1983 humans began engaging in regular mass peace meditations which appear to have quieted solar and geomagnetic activity for a few days after each meditation. International events took a turn for the better around June, 1988 which was a time of some of the largest peace meditations; and solar activity showed a large dip as well. An experimental study on this has been done by The Academy for Peace Research (see Sources Chapter).

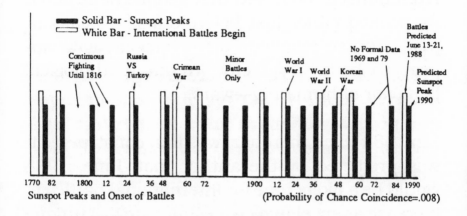

Figure 9. Sunspot Peaks and Onset
of International Battles

Riots, minor battles, and other disturbances, have often, far more often than expected by chance, occurred at times of solar and magnetic disturbances. Figure 10 shows some recent minor events and corresponding magnetic activity. Such patterns occur over and over, although there is not always a one-to-one correspondence between magnetic storms and eruptions of violence. Different magnetic storms appear to have different effects. (More details have been published elsewhere—see references.) Figure 11 also shows some associations between solar activity and adverse events on Earth. These are not isolated instances—such patterns occur over and over, not by chance, but usually coincidental with specific planetary alignments. **The links now appear to be: planetary alignments, increased solar activity, increased geomagnetic activity, biofield changes, hormone changes, and probably changes in brain rhythms leading to hyperemotionalism, errors of judgment, etc.**

This area needs careful investigation, and could lead to different ways of structuring international relations. Wars may be considered more of a pathology than a political, social, or economic conflict. It is the author's hypothesis, based on laboratory research by others, that certain types of magnetic fields trigger hormone changes which increase irritability and aggressive behavior. Wars are usually initiated by males and may be triggered by the hormone, testosterone. Analogous to PMS in females, perhaps we should recognize the existence of MMS (Male Macho Syndrome) in males. Artificial steroids, which are a form of testosterone, taken to increase athletic prowess, are known to produce violence (roid rages) in some males.

Females are affected by the solar-magnetic activity too, but perhaps not as much or in different ways. Females don't usually start wars. More research needs to be done specifically on this topic.

Research on solar activity and planetary magnetism and related effects on Earth's magnetic aura could lead to further breakthroughs in the treatment of disease by magnetic means. It was from just such research that the author was led to develop magnetic devices and use the techniques described in the next chapters.

Since the motions of the planets are predictable, it is possible to forecast solar and GM storms with reasonable accuracy and to take precautionary measures if that seems appropriate.* Some Soviet scientists are reported to have placed critically ill patients in shielded rooms at times of intense solar activity.

---

*A monthly newsletter is now available which gives forecasts for solar activity and magnetic storms based upon planetary positions. See Chapter XI.

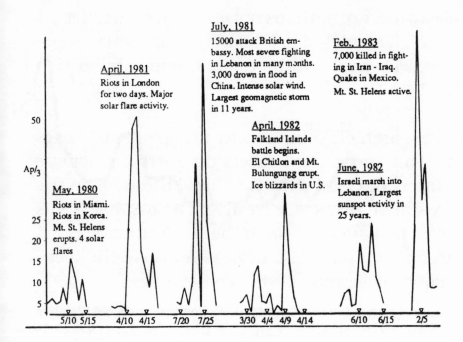

Figure 10. Geomagnetic Storms, A index, Anchorage, Alaska, at
times of Recent World Events

How planets can affect Earth's magnetic field,
other than by direct interference with the solar
wind flow is an exciting and challenging scientific mystery. To refresh the reader's mind we
again reproduce Table 2 to help keep in mind the

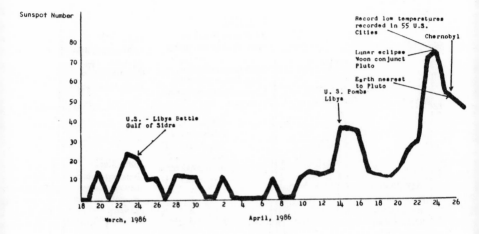

Figure 11. Solar Activity, Libyan-U.S. Conflict, and Cold Weather

possibility that other types of magnetism may exist, since the ordinary magnetic fields around the other planets, except for Jupiter, seem too small to possibly effect Earth. Maybe there are specifically tuned, resonant circuits operating that we have not yet discovered.

TABLE 2

Types of Magnetism	Structural Level
SPIN	Present around all elementary particles. Show interaction with magnetic fields.
IRON	Present in iron and some other metals under certain conditions. Apparently manifests from spin fields that normally cancel each other out in most materials, but not in iron.
ELECTRO-	Manifests when charged particles move together in an organized manner.
ANIMAL	A special type of spin force present around living organisms which interacts with other types of magnetism (see Chapter III).
PLANETARY	Known to be present around Earth and possibly planets (see Chapter IV). Origin unknown.
STELLAR	Present around stars. Origin unknown.

CHAPTER V

MAGNETISM AND LIFE

All living organisms are apparently affected by magnetic field changes. Dr. Frank Brown, a marine biologist who devoted most of his professional career to studying magnetic and other invisible effects on life, informed the author that he believed every cell of every living thing was sensitive to magnetic fields.

Some magnetic field changes produced by solar activity or alignments of the planets are disturbing to people. Other magnetic field patterns are pleasing, calming, or even healing. You can demonstrate some of the effects of magnetic fields for yourself. In the last twenty years some significant advances have been made in the use of magnets for healing. One of the most significant discoveries was made by Albert Davis in 1936. He found that the north and south poles of a magnet had different biological effects. Previous experimenters used powerful horseshoe or electromagnets, placing biological specimens between the poles. Since only small, if any, effects were observed, it was concluded that magnetism had little interaction with living organisms. With what we know now it appears likely that the effects were just cancelling each other out, since they are different for the two poles.

Davis and other researchers eventually established that the south pole of a magnet stimulates plant growth, animal behavior, and biological activity in general, while the north pole calms these functions. Applications of the north pole will retard the growth of bacteria, reduce swelling, pain, inflammation, and increase the alkalinity of a solution. Therefore, different ailments require different magnetic polarities.

Some ailments could be made worse by the application of the wrong polarity.

Do not apply strong magnetic fields indiscriminately to the body, especially the head.

If you don't have magnets or a compass around the house, now is the time to obtain them. You can usually get a compass at a camping supply store or an auto store. You don't need an expensive one. Note that boat and car compasses are marked "North" on the south side as they are meant to be used in front of you as guides. Do not use this type; they are confusing. When you obtain a compass, note the direction of magnetic north in your home or work environment for future reference.

Magnets may be purchased in toy stores, hobby shops, or from industrial supply companies in larger cities. Horseshoe magnets are not useful because you can't separate the poles. Do not depend on the labeling on the magnets—establish this for yourself. I recommend marking the south end with red paint or red nail polish and the north pole with blue.

Magnets used to hold notes on refrigerators, or magnetic cards made of brown plastic often have north and south poles alternating. This may be confusing when you try to establish their polarity with a compass. These magnets are not useful for most diagnosis and treatment.

Determining Magnetic Polarity

Method A. If you have a bar magnet, hang it from a string around the middle. The magnet should swing so that one end points towards Earth's north magnetic pole, that is toward the geographic north. Let us define this as the **south** pole. Mark that end red.

Method B. Bring one side or end of a magnet slowly near the end of a compass needle that is normally pointing north. If the needle swings to your test magnet, define that as the north end of your magnet. Mark that end blue.

Note these definitions. Sometimes confusion results when the terms "north seeking" or "south seeking" are used. Some physics textbooks use the opposite terms in their definitions. To emphasize the difference the terms "biomagnetic north" or "biomagnetic south" will sometimes be used in this book.

Another way of thinking about magnetic polarity is to ask yourself which end of the magnet acts like Earth's north pole with regard to its effect on a compass needle.

Other writers have used the terms "positive" and "negative"; however, since these terms are used for electric phenomena, and have a psychological connotation as well, it is misleading to apply them to magnetic poles. It seems best to keep the tradition of naming the poles of a magnet as we have named the poles of the planet, and to keep in mind the image that our little magnets are labeled like our planet is labeled. After you have identified and marked the poles of your magnets, you are ready to determine their strength.

Determining Magnetic Intensity

Magnetic intensity is usually measured in units called gauss, after a German scientist, Karl Friedrich Gauss (1777-1835) who lived about the time of Mesmer. The Earth's magnetic field is a bit less than one gauss. A magnet used to hold a note to a refrigerator may be about 100 gauss. The one inch diameter ring magnets sold by Radio Shack are about 300 gauss. However, gauss is not the best term because it does not take into account the size and total "magnetic energy" of a magnet. Although the Earth's magnetic field is small, Earth is large, so the total magnetic energy is large. Some tiny magnets used by acupuncturists have a field intensity of several thousand gauss at their surface, but a few inches away, their field strength is only a few gauss. The term "gauss" should always be used in conjunction with the distance from the magnet. There is no simple, inexpensive meter to measure field strength like a volt meter or ammeter, so use the term "gauss" with caution and understanding. By using a magnet of known strength and a compass you can obtain a rough idea of the comparative strength of other magnets. Tables 3 and 4 give some commonly used magnetic terms and strength comparisons.

Now you are ready to do some experiments with magnets.

TABLE 3

Terms Used For Magnetic Field Strength

Tesla	10,000 gauss = one tesla
	This is the largest unit of
	magnetic strength
Gauss	The most commonly used term.
	Ordinary toy magnets have
	gauss strengths of a few hundred.
	Earth's field is about 1/2 gauss.
Gamma	100,000 gamma = one gauss
Femotesla	100 billion femotesla = one gauss
	(A femotesla is one
	quadrillionth of a gauss)

TABLE 4

MAGNETIC FIELD STRENGTHS
OF KNOWN OBJECTS

Objects	Magnetic Field
Planet Earth	0.5-gauss (Variations at times of magnetic storms are about 1/10,000 of this level.)
Typical toy magnet	A few hundred gauss
Large industrial magnets about the size of a video cassette.	1,000 to 3,000 guass
Strongest electromagnets using iron cores	20,000 gauss
Strongest electromagnets using water cooled coils	300,000 gauss in an area about the size of a penny.
White dwarf star	700 million gauss. **Largest known magnetic field.**
Human heart	One millionth of a gauss.
Human brain	One hundred billionth of a gauss.
Bean seed	One trillionth of a gauss?
Electron	One quadrillionth of a bean seed?

EXPERIMENTS WITH MAGNETS

Experiment 1. Plant Growth

Plant several seeds in three separate pots or use three pots in which small seedlings are already growing. Place a south pole of a magnet very close to one plant (you can put it in the soil), north pole near another, and leave the third one as a control. Love and water them equally. Perhaps you will see differences. Several investigators have reported that application of the south pole increases growth rates.

Experiment 2. Altering the Taste of Liquids

Set out three small glasses of water, milk, carbonated beverage, juice, or wine. Place several magnets, north pole up, under one glass, south pole up under another, and leave the third one as a control. After several hours or more of treatment time, have a friend who does not know the treatment procedures, taste the samples. The south pole treatment may increase the acidity of the liquids.

Commercial devices are now available for altering the taste of liquids, especially wine and beer. (See Chapter XI.)

In one experiment to test the effect of magnetic fields on liquids, the author used four glasses of wine. One received north polarity generated by the PULSAR (see next section for photo), the other south polarity, and one was untreated. A fourth glass was treated by a guest who claimed he could improve the taste of wine with his hands. The wine was treated for about 10 minutes. Sceptical, three of us submitted to a blindfolded taste test of the wines. The one the guest had treated was unanimously voted the best tasting. The wine treated with north polarity was judged second best, and the wine treated with south polarity tasted most acrid.

This simple observation supports the notion that the acid-base balance is affected by magnetism. It also supports the finding that a measurable biofield emanates from the hands and this biofield is related to magnetism.

Healers often use their hands to treat people, and their results may be related to their ability to focus their personal biofield, a different type of magnetism, and to alter the water, the acid-base balance, or the complex chemistry within the body.

Experiment 3. Bacterial Growth

Bacteria will flourish in a south pole field. Try treating some food that is on the verge of spoiling with north pole to keep it from getting worse, or south pole to hasten its spoilage. Treat it in a warm place and leave it for several days.

Experiment 4. Treating Fruit

In one series of experiments, the author repeatedly used three oranges at a time, one treated with a north pole pulsing field, the other south, and one control. After 36 hours of treatment there were clear differences in the taste of the oranges. The north pole treatments consistently produced the sweetest taste. Try the experiment yourself... perhaps with lemons!

How magnetic fields affect living organisms is an ongoing research topic all over the world. A hundred years ago it was believed that life did not respond to magnetic fields because no effects were observed no matter how large a magnetic field was applied. Researchers like Frank Brown recognized that, since living organisms exist in a highly variable, yet small amplitude magnetic field, they would respond best to magnetic field changes on the same order of magnitude. His approach led to positive research results. Brown detected and measured magnetic responses in a variety of marine animals such as oysters, brine shrimp, mud snails, etc. as well as other life forms such as earthworms, mice, rats, hamsters, and fruit flies.

He found that many animals had biological clocks tuned to the moon, sun, tides (which are a combination of the sun and moon, direction of magnetic north, and variations of the geomagnetic field). In one experiment he and his co-workers measured 51,000 snail tracks to determine their ability to distinguish magnetic direction. Their paths were altered by application of magnetic fields from 0-2- gauss and were most sensitive when the applied field was closest to the natural GM field strength.

The oxygen consumption of potatoes was found

by Brown to greatly fluctuate on a daily basis. This too, was assumed to be related to geomagnetic variations.

Sharks, whales, rays, many species of bacteria, a type of green algae, pigeons, butterflies, and honey bees also have been found to show sensitivity to magnetic fields. James Gould, a biologist at Princeton University, noted indirect evidence that the sensitivity of bees and pigeons seems to be hundreds or even thousands of times better than would be necessary merely to determine compass direction. Gould observed that pigeons are disoriented when released in areas of magnetic anomaly at times of GM storms. These changes are on the order of a few hundred thousandths of Earth's base field. How this sensitivity is achieved is not known. However it is reasonable to assume that pigeons, like other living organisms, have a spin force or biofield which is responsive to, or co-varies with, geomagnetic activity. At times of magnetic storms the direction of the spin force can reverse. This certainly could account for the observed disorientation in pigeons. The areas of magnetic anomaly such as Iron Mountain in northern Rhode Island, should be investigated with a biofield meter. Perhaps the spin force around a human would be different there. The author found that the biofield is different at different places on the Earth, but more careful research needs to be undertaken.

Homing pigeons must have a magnetic map as well in order to navigate as accurately as they do. Particles of magnetite have been found in pigeons, salmon, and sharks, but not in humans. Gould and other researchers found that each bee had approximately 1 million small crystals of magnetite located in front of the abdomen. These crystals appear to be synthesized (as they do in other animals). Pigeons have between 10 and 100 times as much magnetic material as bees, but none has been found in humans, who must use compasses to find their way home!

Nevertheless, humans are very sensitive to magnetic fields as you will see by performing the experiments described in the next section.

Experiment 5. Cleaning the "Aura"

Take a strong magnet (1,000 gauss) or set of several ring magnets stacked together and wipe the aura or biofield of a willing subject. That is, move the magnet in very slow strokes from head to the feet, one or two inches away from the body. You can use stroking motions as if you were using a hairbrush. Go all around the body. Use only one pole. Ask the person if they experience any sensations.

Then switch roles and poles and let them magnetically stroke your aura. Try this with several people. Ask if anyone experiences sensations.

Some people will report sensations or feelings from this process. The sensations will be different for each person, but the poles may have a characteristically different effect. People often report a soothing feeling from being stroked by north poles and a stimulating feeling from being stroked by the south poles. In general women are more aware of the changes and sensations of magnetic fields than men. People who are out of balance or ill perceive sensations more readily than healthy individuals.

Generally, if a person has some specific ache or pain, stiff muscle, malfunctioning organ or gland, broken bone, or old injury that hasn't fully healed, they may perceive some sensation around that area when stroked by a magnet. This constitutes a crude form of diagnosis which we will formalize in the next section.

DIAGNOSIS WITH MAGNETS

About fifteen years ago, it was discovered that muscles strengthen and weaken depending on stimuli applied to the body such as different foods, herbs, or other chemicals. Thought patterns, or even the close presence of another person may also strengthen or weaken certain muscles.

This procedure of testing muscles for strength has been called "Applied Kinesiology". Another common name is "Touch for Health". Muscle testing, as it has popularly come to be called, has been used extensively to diagnose the condition of organs and glands.

Dr. Richard Broeringmeyer (see sources), a chiropractor who has been researching magnetic healing for many years, discovered that muscle testing can be used effectively and efficiently to diagnose the functioning of the glands and organs of the body. Dr. Broeringmeyer found that any muscle will test strong or weak when a north or south magnetic field (not both at once) is applied to any gland or organ or part of the body, if that part is not functioning properly. He commonly uses an extended arm strength test, or a simple lower leg extension test (see illustrations).

Dr. Broeringmeyer found that magnetic diagnosis procedures are quicker, and as accurate, as any other system he has studied. The author, although initially skeptical, has come to the same conclusions using pulsed magnetic field instruments. The reader is invited to make his or her own investigations.

Dr. Broeringmeyer has designed a special monophase polarized magnet specifically for diagnosis (see Chapter XI, Bio Health Enterprises). The PULSAR designed by the author will also work well for diagnosis (see Chapter VI). A long bar magnet or cylindrical magnetic will also work, although perhaps not as well.

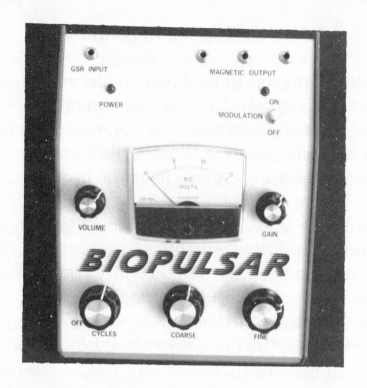

The BIO PULSAR - A Pulsed Magnetic Field Generator

The BIO PULSAR has a small applicator about the size of a palm which is applied to the body for diagnosis or for treatment. The two sides of the applicator are colored red and blue to designate south and north poles. The PULSAR is very easy to use; waveform, frequency, and intensity can be independently varied. Power is supplied by re-chargeable batteries, good for 1,000 charges.

Muscle Testing Procedure

Ask the person to lie down on their back and raise one arm straight up. Ask them to gently close the hand into a fist. To begin, explain that you are going to move their arm down towards their hip and they are to resist as hard as they can. Before you apply any force, say in a clear, loud tone, "Lock - and resist." Most people will automatically hold their breath at this point. You should wait 1/2 a second, then push or pull their arm down a few inches towards their hip. Carefully make a mental note of how strongly they can resist and whether or not you feel the arm locked solidly in place. Then apply the magnet or magnetic applicator systematically to each gland or organ in turn, using first one side or polarity, and then the other. Muscle test each magnetic polarity - to determine the different strengthening or weakening effects. Make a note of each place of weakness for later treatment.

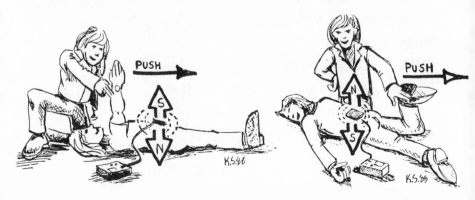

Magnets or magnetic applicators can be applied over the clothing for diagnosis or treatment.

Here are some tips to help you get consistent and reproducible results:

1. Apply pressure at the same place on a person's arm—usually at the wrist.
2. Always place yourself in the same body position and use, for example only two or three fingers to push or pull.
3. Be firm and clear in your statement to "Lock...and resist.", and always test at the same time after you give the command.
4. Ask the person being tested not to look at you; they may close their eyes.
5. Allow a rest for the arm after a few tests. You can switch arms.
6. Watch their face when you muscle test. The body is so wonderfully designed that, if a person's muscle does go weak, other muscles will automatically take over the task. However the person may make a grimace as other muscles compensate, so you will know that a weakening of the primary muscle has occurred.
7. Always ask the person which polarity feels stronger, especially if there is no obvious difference. People usually know when they are stronger or weaker and it is good to encourage their awareness in the procedure.

FRONT VIEW: TEST POINTS

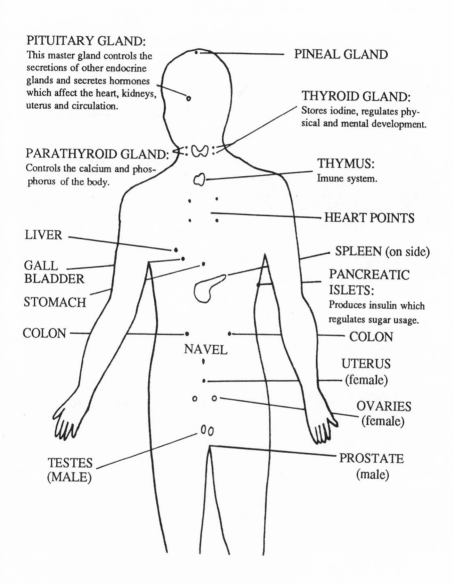

PITUITARY GLAND:
This master gland controls the
secretions of other endocrine
glands and secretes hormones
which affect the heart, kidneys,
uterus and circulation.

PINEAL GLAND

THYROID GLAND:
Stores iodine, regulates physical and mental development.

PARATHYROID GLAND:
Controls the calcium and phosphorus of the body.

THYMUS:
Imune system.

HEART POINTS

LIVER

SPLEEN (on side)

GALL
BLADDER

PANCREATIC
ISLETS:
Produces insulin which
regulates sugar usage.

STOMACH

COLON

COLON

NAVEL

UTERUS
(female)

OVARIES
(female)

TESTES
(MALE)

PROSTATE
(male)

BACK VIEW

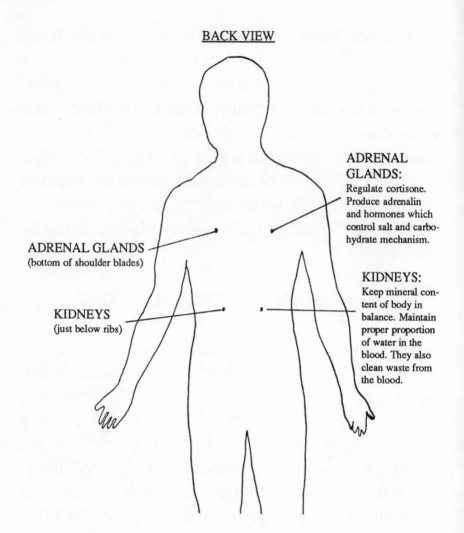

ADRENAL GLANDS:
Regulate cortisone. Produce adrenalin and hormones which control salt and carbohydrate mechanism.

ADRENAL GLANDS
(bottom of shoulder blades)

KIDNEYS:
Keep mineral content of body in balance. Maintain proper proportion of water in the blood. They also clean waste from the blood.

KIDNEYS
(just below ribs)

After you have completed the tests on the front of the body, ask the person to turn over and test the adrenals and kidneys. For these test points, use the leg, lifted up and bent at the knee (see illustration). Push the foot back towards the floor and ask the person to resist as before. Note that the test points for the adrenals, which are located just below the shoulder blades, are not where the adrenals are located. The adrenals are actually just above the kidneys.

Leg Length As A Diagnostic Test

You may also use leg length as a test. This has the advantage of taking the client's psychological state out of the testing procedure. No resisting effort is required. Simply lift both legs (the client lies on their back) and check to see if one leg contracts due to the presence of the test magnetic field. The contraction may be as much as a quarter of an inch and is easily perceived. The client may be barefooted or shod. If there is a contraction, treatment with the opposite polarity is indicated.

It may be helpful before beginning this procedure to lift both legs and give them a gentle tug and a shake, then lower them, check the lengths with no magnetic test pole applied, and then begin the testing procedure. The disadvantage of this method is that it is a bit more awkward and takes a little more time. It can be useful to confirm the arm muscle test.

Finger Strength as a Diagnostic Test

A very simple, yet remarkably accurate muscle test uses just one finger and thumb. Have the client push thumb and forefinger or middle finger together as tightly as possible while leaving the other fingers extended. Then give a verbal signal such as "resist" and attempt to pull them apart. Note the strength of resistance when the north pole or south pole is applied to the test point. Treat with the side which makes the person stronger.

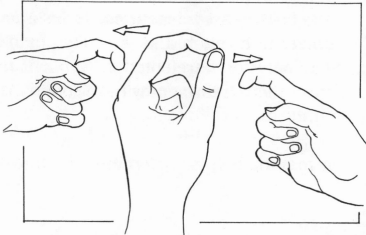

General Comments About Muscle Testing

When a gland or organ is overactive, a muscle test will show a weakening when the biomagnetic south pole of a magnet is placed at that point. If a muscle is weakened when the north pole is placed over the test point, the organ is underactive according to Dr. Broeringmeyer, who has written an extensive manual on testing (see references).

For example, Dr. Broeringmeyer has been diagnosing and treating stomach ailments with magnets for several years. By holding the magnet over the stomach and testing muscle strength one can determine whether that organ is hypoactive or hyperactive.

A hypo or underactive stomach has become more alkaline than normal in its response to the body's demand on it. There is less acidity and digestion is slowed down. The hydrogen ion concentration has apparently been decreased. When the north pole of a diagnostic magnet is placed on the stomach, the body is weakened because the problem is made worse by further decreasing the hydrogen ion. The north polarity makes fruit sweeter, by decreasing the hydrogen ion concentration.

When the stomach is too acidic, it will be over-active. The hydrogen ion level is higher than it needs to be. When the south pole of a diagnostic magnetic is placed on the stomach the condition is made worse and the body's muscles are weakened. A person with a hyper or too acidic stomach is prone to ulcers.

Under normal conditions, the body does not react differently on exposure to magnetic fields. The body can quickly correct any temporary imbalance imposed by the magnetic fields and return to equilibrium. Healthy people working around 10,000 gauss fields do not experience any abnormal effects at all.

Clients sometimes know which gland or organ is out of balance because they have had medical tests or sensations, or pains in those areas. When knowledge like that has been available it has almost always validated the muscle testing procedure. However, muscle testing is not infallible and does not always indicate treatment polarity. Sometimes the mind set of the client will alter the results. Occasionally the person may be too ill to be tested. If the condition is marginal, the test will be inconclusive.

Any place on the body can be used as a test point for magnetic treatments—the principle is the same. Simply place the magnetic applicator on that point and test muscle strength. If one polarity increases strength then treat with that polarity. If you know acupuncture, use the meridians, if you know polarity therapy, use the polarity points, if you know reflexology, you can use the tender foot points. If you don't know, experiment. Anywhere there is a tender spot on the body, you can try magnetic treatment. You'll probably find out something not yet discovered. The human body is the most complex thing in the world. No one has yet discovered why muscles weaken or legs change their length in response to stimuli. Can you figure it out?

In the past decade, direct detection of magnetic fields, from the organs of the body, have been made using an extremely sensitive magnetic detector called a SQUID. The fields from the body organs are small—less than one millionth of a gauss. Compare this with any magnet you happen to have around the house which may be typically several hundred gauss. SQUID detectors are expensive and must be used under carefully controlled laboratory conditions. While useful information is obtained in this manner, it is not a match for the quick and simple method presented in this book. The SQUID system will not detect changes in glands, either.

Magnetic stimulation of the brain's motor nerve section has been used to diagnose nervous system disorders. In this application, a coil on top of the head is energized by a 5,000 volt pulse. This creates a large magnetic field which in turn produces minute electric currents which triggers twitches in the hands and feet if the nervous system is in proper order. This is completely different from the diagnostic applications described in this chapter.

Neither the SQUID nor MRI (Magnetic Resonance Image - see Chapter VII) systems involve treatment. In the coming years this technology, combined with material presented in this book, probably will come closer together and we will have some powerful ways to treat all types of ailments. The following chapters will give you some idea of what has been achieved to date.

CHAPTER VI

MAGNETISM AND
MAGNETIC DEVICES

To say that some condition is treated with magnetism is a vague statement, for magnets come in many different shapes and strengths. Hundreds of years ago only natural magnets or lodestones were available. Gradually people learned to make iron, and therefore magnets, in different forms. The horseshoe magnet was a common shape for many years, but it isn't very effective for healing purposes. When electricity was used to produce permanent magnets, they could be made much stronger. In the early part of this century it was discovered that if iron was mixed with nickel, aluminum and cobalt it would hold an even stronger field. These powerful magnets were called Alnico magnets and for many years they were the kings of magnetism, enabling powerful generators and permanent magnet motors to be made. Alnico magnets lose their magnetic strength over time unless they are stored with a magnetic keeper or kept in place in the generator or motor.

About 25 years ago, it was found that the addition of the element samarium and other so-called rare earth elements had the capacity to lock cobalt atoms into an exceptionally tight formation and keep them that way.

Although cobalt is not as good a natural magnet as iron, when combined with samarium, the result is a magnetic material more powerful per pound of weight than the previous mixtures of nickel and iron (Alnico magnets), and one which will hold the magnetic orientation for a long time.

These mixtures of elements could be made in powdered form and then melted and cast into any desired shape. They could be mixed with other materials, ground into very flat or precise surfaces, and then highly magnetized by placing them in properly shaped current carrying coils. This has greatly expanded the industrial and technical uses for magnets. The use of magnets for healing purposes is strictly a secondary consideration; until recent years few people considered them of any biological value or significance.

Within the last few years another improvement in producing more powerful magnetic materials was made by scientists at General Motors. Called MAGNAQUENCH, they are alloys of iron, boron, and neodymium that retain magnetism better than any other material yet discovered. These magnets are also cheaper than the cobalt-samarium magnets and are now being used in car starters. They are not yet available for general consumer use, although similar materials have been developed in Japan, called NEOMAX, which are now becoming available.

Caution should be exercised in the application of magnetic fields. Unless the proper polarity and configuration is selected, relief from pain may be more by accident than by design. Bigger and stronger is not necessarily better. While many configurations of permanent magnets are commercially available, few are useful for biological applications. The chances of a successful treatment with just any randomly chosen magnet are probably about 10% according to Broeringmeyer.

Initially people treated ailments with whatever type of magnet they could obtain. No attention was paid to polarity, or if it was, people mistakenly believed that one had to make a complete 'magnetic circuit', analogous to a complete electric circuit, by placing the north pole on one side of the area to be treated and the south pole on the other side.* In the early part of this century it was discovered that the different poles of a magnet, that is, different spin directions, had different biological effects and a significant advance was made in the use of magnetism for effective healing. In the past, people believed that they had to use large and heavy, or big and strong magnets to treat various conditions. Now they can choose from a wide variety of shapes, sizes and strengths.

---

*This erroneous belief comes from an incorrect view of magnetism. Behind this belief is the assumption that something flows from one magnetic pole to another. This notion has also led to the concept that magnetic field lines have an independent existence and that they must be closed or always return to the opposite pole. These beliefs are still common today and lead to confusion when experimental data provides contrary information.

When it is recognized that magnetic fields are a form of spin fields, the search for magnetic monopoles will cease, for it is like looking for the back of your hand in a place separate from the front. Although a lot of money has been spent on this Zen koan of science, it probably won't lead to enlightenment.

Permanent magnets have three possible variations: polarity, strength, and physical size. You can have a small srong magnet (more expensive) or a large weaker magnet, or a large and strong magnet (expensive). Permanent ceramic magnets can be of practically any shape, and commonly available forms are horseshoe, bar, round, ring, or flat rectangles. There are also a wide variety of magnetic materials made by mixing magnetic particles with plastic or artificial rubber in the form of brown strips or sheets. These materials are often used for refrigerator door seals, magnetic calendars, business cards, etc. These usually have alternating polarities and are not very effective for healing purposes.

There is a common belief that bigger (and stronger) is better, but that is not always the case for optimum biological effects. Living organisms evolved in the Earth's changing field, which, while extensive, is not strong. Changes in the Earth's magnetic field which are biologically significant, as we saw in Chapter IV, are less than a ten-thousandth of a gauss. Some people have speculated that the geomagnetic field carries information somehow used by our organism. At present we don't know how to read the code. If this is so, and I think it is, then we are in for another breakthrough in healing when we crack the code. The code may be related to the different types of planetary magnetism as discussed in Chapter IV which apparently have different effects on our hormone system and brain waves.

These considerations suggest that the development of electronic magnets of varying waveforms may prove to be more effective in the treatment of injuries and diseases than permanent magnets.

ELECTRONIC MAGNETS

More flexibility and precision of magnetic parameters is possible with the use of electronic magnets. This has greatly expanded the possibilities for magnetotherapy, but it has made it a lot more complicated too.

To simply say that something is magnetic, or produces a magnetic field is not complete; at least four parameters must be specified to fully describe an electrically generated magnetic field. These are:

1. Field strength, usually measured in gauss.

2. Polarity; whether it is always one polarity or oscillates from one to the other.

3. Frequency, usually measured in hertz (hz) or cycles per second (cps).

4. Repetition rate or pulse rate—also measured in cycles per second.

The frequency of a pulsating magnetic field can be anything from millions of cycles per second (radar frequencies) to less than one per second. Moreover, to simply say the frequency of a pulsating field is so many cycles per second can be misleading for the actual waveform may be complex. For example, a pulse of 20 cycles per second, may be a smooth sine wave (rarely), a square wave, a sawtooth wave, a spike wave, or practically any other complex pattern. All such different shapes or complex mixtures of waves may be differentially important for biological systems.

There are thousands and thousands of different waveforms that an electronic magnetic field can have; as many different forms as there are different types of musical sounds. In fact the analogy is quite apt, for a radio speaker operates by producing a magnetic field which in turn moves a speaker cone to vibrate air molecules and produce the complex sounds we hear. Just as some sounds or types of music are discordant, and others harmonious, some patterns of magnetic fields are disturbing (as when Earth's magnetic field is "stormy") and other patterns of magnetic fields are soothing and help the body heal. No one knows what waveforms work best, but it is known that rectified, or monopolar pulses between 10 and 20 cycles per second are quite effective.

The development of electronically generated magnetic fields will give people the capability to find those special patterns that are optimum for facilitating the healing process. More research will be needed to find the optimum waveforms.

TYPES OF MAGNETIC DEVICES

Permanent Magnets

Acupuncturists use tiny, high gauss ceramic cobalt magnets about the size of a BB. These come on sticky tape and can be applied directly on the skin. Acupuncturists generally use them on the acupuncture points, but they can be applied anywhere on the body.

A number of magnetic bands, pocket magnets, discs, polarized magnets, back magnets, etc. are available from Mid -American Marketing in Ohio.

Magnetic jewelry, made in Japan, consists of gold plated ceramic magnets which can be hung around the neck or wrists. These are usually composed of small magnets about the size of a pencil eraser head and are strung together. Both polarities are present and the configuration can-not be altered. They apparently help some people, but not everyone.

In Europe, a magnetic foil has been developed that can be applied to the body like a healing plaster. The best clinical results have been found with pains of the back, neck, and joints.

Permanent magnets of all shapes and sizes are available from industrial supply houses, hard-ware stores, and speciality houses. Polarity should be checked with a compass on such magnets even if they are marked, because some people use the terms 'north seeking' and 'north' interchangeably. Horseshoe magnets and circular speaker magnets have not been found effective for promoting healing according to Dr. Broeringmeyer. His organization, Bio Health Enterprises, supplies different types of magnets suitable for energy balancing and diagnosis (see Chapter XI).

Two BioMagnetic Kits, one for students, and one for professionals, are now available from PsychoPhysics Labs. Made by Dowling Magnetic, they contain a variety of permanent magnets of different strengths and shapes. A manual accompanies each kit which describes experiments that can be done on living organisms.

Magnetic pads and pillows of various sizes are also available. Some of these take into account polarity and some do not. It's probably more effective to properly diagnose the body as described in Chapter V, and treat accordingly. However it may be possible for the body to benefit from either polarity depending on its needs. That was the approach of the inventor of the magnetic beds described in the next section.

Edward Kaufman, a healer in Southern California, maintains that the body will take what it needs if offered both poles at once. He has designed small oval shaped magnets about the size of the top of a thumbtack called Magnet tabs, which have the north pole on one end and south pole on the other. They are attached to a piece of sticky tape and place on the body over the glands or organs.

The Magnetic Sleeping System

The magnetic sleeping system was designed by a Japanese physician. It was derived from a trial and error system of taping magnets on the body and observing the effects. The magnetic beds have small permanent magnets implanted in a firm pad at about 4 inch intervals. Additional magnets are in a pillow and a down comforter. In order to provide both north and south polarities special double magnets are used which have a north and a south pole forced together (called 'buck magnets'). The individual magnets in the bed have strengths of 700-850 gauss; they are not physically large magnets, and the overall magnetic field experienced by the sleeper is only a few times that of Earth's natural magnetic field.

The bed is also well designed to provide optimum support for the spine and muscular system, which in itself greatly helps people to maintain their health. Many people have greatly benefited by using these beds.

The magnetic sleeping system is a great advance over the water bed and electric blankets which have been shown to produce harmful effects in people due to the nature of the 60 cycle electromagnetic field.

Research on the benefits of the beds is being undertaken by Psycho Physics Labs and people who would like to participate in the research and/or purchase a bed for their own use may receive a free demonstration by writing the company (see Chapter XI). The research procedure will include an endocrine and organ diagnosis and a simple questionnaire.

A magnetic chair and a simple bed has been designed by a Dowling Miner Magnetics Corporation in California. These devices have only the biomagnetic north pole available and therefore are useful for helping people destress.

Pulsed Magnetic Field Instruments

The POCKET PULSAR is shown in the illustration. An electronic circuit, powered by rechargeable batteries, generates a unique, pulsing waveform. It's design evolved over a three year period of experimentation with different types of coils and waveforms. It produces monopolar pulses of a complex waveform. The repetition rate of the complex pulse is set to about 13 hz. To use it the applicator is simply placed over the gland or organ or site of pain or injury, and a diagnosis is made as described in Chapter V. Then the same applicator is applied for treatments from 15 to 30 minutes once or twice a day.

A more sophisticated instrument, the BIOPULSAR is available which can vary repetition rate, frequency, and waveform. The average field strength at the surface of the palm sized applicator is about three gauss. Polarity of the applicator is simply changed by turning the applicator over; the north polarity side is colored blue and the south, red.

By use of the proper electrodes, the BIOPULSAR can also be used for introducing pulsed electric currents in the body which are useful for helping some conditions heal more quickly. This a separate area of study which won't be discussed in detail in this book.

The BIOPULSAR is also a fully functional GSR biofeedback instrument. A separate book -BIO-MEDITATION- on the many uses of GSR biofeedback has been written by the author (see Chapter XI).

The professional model BIOPULSAR can be used to test the effects of different frequencies, waveforms, strengths, and pulse rates. By varying these and using simple muscle strength tests or subjective reports of the patient, one can search for optimal healing patterns. Some people claim that each type of injury or disease, gland or organ, will respond differently to different frequencies. This does not seem to be a critical factor in the experience of the author and, independently, of Dr. Laurence Badgley, who said there is no magic frequency in the healing process. Research by others has shown that a pulse rate of between 10 and 20 works well, but some people claim that different ailments respond to different frequencies. This is a vast territory for the independent researcher to explore.

Dr. Badgley has designed a unique pulsed magnetic field instrument that detects a person's heart beat and administers a magnetic pulse at a repetition rate synchronized to the heart beat. His instrument uses two applicators about the size of large spools of thread which are placed on the front and back of the body or limb area to be treated. He has made substantial contributions to the subject of energy medicine and has a book available by that title (see Chapter XI).

A Canadian Company called Magna-Pak markets an elaborate German made pulsed magnetic field device which can treat several sites at once with varying waveform patterns.

A firm in New Jersey called Elec Biology makes a large coil system that wraps around an arm or leg or even the entire torso. Their instruments are not sold, only leased and apparently do not take into account magnetic polarity. They are frequently used for sports injuries.

Some whole body treatment devices have been made in Sweden. A person lays within large coils thru which electric currents surge and pulse creating various types of magnetic fields which penetrate the entire body. Amazingly beneficial results have been reported from the use of these instruments but they are expensive and not available in the United States.

Several other pulsed magnetic field instruments are available and many have been used in Europe, India, Japan, and China, where research on magnetic healing has been going on for many years.

In the 30's and 40's a number of instruments were developed to produce magnetic healing. Some of these were perceived as fraudulent and the FDA curtailed their use. Yet there was a kernel of validity in their results, even though the scientific basis for their operation was unknown. As of 1989, the FDA has given approval to some magnetic devices for healing of non-union fractures. The Japanese equivalent of the FDA has approved both pulsed magnetic field instruments and permanent magnets for healing purposes.

Pulsed Versus Permanent Magnets

No controlled study has been done, to my knowledge, comparing the effectiveness of pulsed versus permanent magnetic fields for healing specific ailments. One researcher reported that the PULSAR was twice as effective as permanent magnets and that the effects of treatments lasted much longer. Perhaps this is because the body seems to adapt to any stimulus that is constant and quickly ignores magnetic fields that are unchanging. Magnetic necklaces shift around as a person moves so the field would vary, although the presence of both polarities is not ideal. During sleep a person frequently moves around, so the fields produced by the tiny magnets in the magnetic sleeping system would be perceived as varying by the body.

On the other hand, magnets taped to the skin might quickly lose their effectiveness, if variation of the field is an important parameter. If the generation of minute electric currents were the only mechanism by which healing took place, then pulsed magnetic fields should work more effectively than permanent magnets, since permanent magnets taped to the body would not generate any significant electric currents. Since multiple mechanisms are involved (see Chapter IX), combinations of permanent and pulsed magnetic fields may prove to be the most effective treatment modality. Our present instruments may only be crude bludgeons compared to what may be developed in the future.

Electrotherapy Instruments

Electrotherapy devices inject electricity directly into the body. Two electrodes are necessary and must be attached directly to the surface of the skin, unlike magnetic fields which can be applied by only one applicator which need not touch the skin. The currents used by electrotherapy instruments vary from 20 microamperes to 4,000 microamperes (4 milliamperes). As in the case of pulsed magnetic fields, many different wave forms, frequencies, and pulse repetition rates are used. Electrotherapy devices are useful for sports injuries, soft tissue injuries, healing of fractures, and many other ailments. Magnetic fields, however seem to help more ailments.

Although there is some overlap between electrotherapy and magnetotherapy, the mechanisms

of healing are completely different. Magnetotherapy is easier to use because only one applicator
is needed and that can be applied over clothing.
Comparison studies between electrotherapy and
magnetotherapy have not been made.

The BIOPULSAR can be used for either electrotherapy or magnetotherapy or both at once. It is
very easy to use in any modality over a wide range
of current and waveforms.

Non-Equivalence of
Electrotherapy and Magnetotherapy

Although both magnetic and electric treatments
may be used simultaneously, they are NOT equivalent and cannot be used interchangeably. While
it is true that electric currents generate magnetic
fields and vice versa as described in Chapter II,
the types of currents typically used to treat the
body do not produce a magnetic field anywhere
near the magnitude of magnetic fields used for
treatments, nor is it apt to be of the right polarity
or even applied in the appropriate place.

Pulsed magnetic fields will create electric currents wherever there are ions, but it is question-

able whether or not these electric currents could be in the right direction and of the right strength to properly augment the healing process. Bassett has used pulsed magnetic fields to successfully treat fractures and he maintains that these magnetic fields create microelectric currents which in turn initiates the healing process. He notes that electric currents have been shown to help fractures heal, but it is not always easy to place electrodes on the bone or skin surface in the optimum manner, whereas magnetic fields can be externally applied even over casts to generate currents within the bone. However, permanent magnets also help fractures heal, so there must be other factors operating besides the production of electric currents.

Research on electrotherapy, as is the case with magnetotherapy, is going on all over the world. We shall not attempt to cover that subject in this book but will continue with a summary of research on magnetism and healing.

CHAPTER VII

RESEARCH ON MAGNETIC FIELD TREATMENTS

Magnetic fields are now used to help the body heal more ailments than any other single treatment modality. A list of some ailments known to be helped by magnetic field treatments is shown below:

All acute injuries such
as breaks, burns, sprains,
pains, whiplash, etc.
All types of glandular disease
Alzheimer's disease
Anxiety attacks
Arthritis (some types)
Asthma
Bladder weakness
Brain injuries
Bursitis
Cancer (some types)
Cerebral Palsy
Cataracts
Contusions
Diabetes
Diverticulitis
Fracture Repair

Gall bladder disease
Glaucoma
Headaches
Kidney disease
Liver disease
Lower back pain
Multiple Sclerosis.
Pancreatic disease
Premenstrual cramps
Prostrate disease
Schizophrenia
Sinus Congestion
Spleen Malfunction
Stiff Shoulder
Stomach upsets
Temper Tantrums
Unginitis
Vertigo

There is a steadily increasing number of reports on the healing of different ailments with magnetic fields. One person can scarcely keep up with the research, especially on a world wide basis. The number of conditions, injuries, ailments, or diseases treated by magnetic fields seems to be continuously expanding. In the Soviet Union over 2,000 reports have been published on magneto-biology, as it's called there. Magnets are used to speed wound healing after operations, to improve blood circulation, and to strengthen bones. Long term tests showed no harm to any organs or body tissues or functions. In Europe 50,000 patients a year receive magnetic treatments according to one report.

Among all the published reports, though, only a few have been carefully performed using double blind studies, control groups, placebo techniques, and statistical analyses. This is not surprising since it takes a great deal of time, money, and careful attention to many details to do a thorough study of anything. When one is dealing with something as complex as human behavior it can require dozens of studies to definitely "prove" anything. A critical sceptic can usually find something wrong with any single study. In working with people there are always psychological complications. People will often behave so as to thwart the study just out of orneriness, even when it isn't to their advantage. Or people will be so willing to believe that something will help them get better that they will improve no matter what the treatment. The placebo effect is so well known that sugar pills are a prescription item.

In addition to those factors, the author has repeatedly observed people who have quickly and dramatically improved from magnetic treatment or some other remedy, only to rapidly fall back to their original state of poor health in a few days or weeks. Initially puzzled by this, it was eventually recognized that some people have created their illness for some uniquely personal reasons; or they get some psychological, social, or economic value from it, and they want to remain as they are, even if that seems to be a miserable state to an outside observer. A severely ill person is often intertwined in a network of family and friends with carefully developed interactions, so if he or she rapidly improves, all those social interactions must change. This can be too difficult for some people to manage—it's easier to stay ill.

In addition to all the psychological factors which can obscure the efficacy of magnetic field treatments, there is the question of what particular type, strength, waveform, or pulse repetition rate works best. Some researchers have built their own devices which may not be easily duplicated by anyone else. Or, even if a commercially available instrument was used, details of the magnetic field are not always published. Manufacturers of instruments may not publish them, and it's not easy to make accurate measurements of small magnetic field strengths and waveforms. Therefore one can't be sure what type of treatment the patient actually received. Polarity is seldom mentioned in much of the literature, yet it is a very important variable.

In spite of so many difficulties, the evidence is overwhelmingly positive in supporting the notion that magnetic fields, in all their variations and permutations, are of enormous benefit to human health.

One of the more careful studies was published in the medical journal Lancet in 1984. Twenty-nine people with shoulder pains that had not responded to steroid and other conventional measures, were divided into two groups. For four weeks one group received pulsed magnetic field treatments, the other half a placebo. After four weeks both groups received magnetic treatments. Frequency was set at 73 hz, but the polarity was not specified, and it was not clear if the patients received alternating or monopolar fields. By the end of the study 19 of the 29 patients were symptomless and 5 others much improved.

Dr. Ulrich Warnke published a study in 1980 on the application of 20 hz magnetic fields of about 50 gauss to the head (polarity unspecified). By taking infrared thermographs he found that arms and hands showed an increase in blood flow within two minutes. Dissolved oxygen in the blood tissues was also increased by a factor of two. Apparently the blood vessels widened and the oxygen carrying capacity of the blood increased. Since many ailments benefit from increased blood flow and increased oxygen, such general magnetic treatments can be very helpful. Other studies and reports confirm the observation that oxygen utilization is increased.

A study published in 1989 in the journal Psychoenergetics reported an 80% improvement in multiple sclerosis patients. This was a double blind study using nearly 100 patients. Pulsed magnetic fields were used, but polarity was not specified.

Dr. Tetsuro Okino at the Teikyko Medical School in Japan carried out a study using permanent magnets for shoulder pains and stiff necks. Of 80 people treated, about 30% found them very effective and another 60% reported them effective. A control group of 25 people were treated with fake magnets. No one reported the fake magnets were very effective, but 29% reported that they were somewhat effective, so there is definitely a placebo effect. This seems high, however Japanese people are even more trained to give socially desirable or polite and expected answers than members of occidental races.

A study with significant implications was done by Bassett and Ito on nerve regeneration in 77 rats. They used magnetic fields (gauss strength not stated) pulsing at 72 hz. Nerve regeneration was improved by a factor of two over a 14 week treatment period. Such positive effects could apply to humans as well. Dr. Benjamin Lau of Loma Linda University in San Diego found 16 of 19 patients with osteoarthritis reported absence of stiffness after six weeks of magnetic treatment. In another group of 23 osteoarthritic patients with severe pain, 20 were pain free at the end of 6 weeks while the other 3 reported only mild and tolerable pain. Dr. Lau also treated 16 people with sports injuries. Half received fake treatments for the first 4 weeks. All improved when given real treatments, after only 6 or 8 sessions.

Everywhere around the world magnetism is now being used to help the healing process. Permanent magnets of all shapes and sizes, instruments generating dozens of different waveforms,—they all help some people with some conditions beyond any reasonable doubts and over and above placebo effects.

In Puyallup, Washington, a little town near Seattle, a dentist, Jack Prince, published an excellent report on the use of tiny, but high strength magnets placed on acupuncture points to reduce bleeding, gagging and sensitivity to the pain of dental work.

In North Carolina, Dr. Goesta Wollin has successfully treated three cases of breast cancer using super strong Neomax magnets from Japan. Although magnetic field therapy is expected to revolutionize the treatment of some types of cancer, home treatment is inadvisable.

INCORRECT POLARITY COULD MAKE A TUMOR GROW MORE VIGOROUSLY. DO NOT USE SOUTH POLARITY MAGNETS (AS DEFINED IN THIS BOOK) ON TUMORS.

An international conference on magnetic healing was held at The Institute of Magnetotherapy in Madras, India in 1987. About 30 papers were presented describing magnetic treatments for the typical kinds of ailments mentioned in this chapter. All reports were positive. One unusual report was on the application of PMF (pulsed magnetic fields) for treatment of severe cold injuries. Three groups of rats were tested; one group exposed to severe cold and not treated with PMF, took about 4 weeks to heal, a second group, exposed to cold and treated with PMF for 30 minutes every day, took only 10-12 days to heal. The third group was treated with PMF before being exposed to cold. This group had only slight injuries and became normal in about a week.

About twenty years ago the author had frostbite on one finger. After two years all effects disappeared only to reappear about three years ago as a white finger when the hand or body was exposed to cold. Four treatments with the PULSAR (south polarity) eliminated the symptom for over a year. After two more treatments, it has not reappeared.

The idea of magnetic field treatments for prevention of disease is important and has been mentioned by other researchers. Davis and Rawls pretreated mice with permanent magnetic fields and found that the pretreated mice could not be successfully inoculated with cancer carrying cells, whereas normally mice will readily take on cancer from inoculations.

In another study carried out in France, mice were infected with a parasite which usually results in death within four days. But when the mice were treated by a modulated magnetic field of 1200 gauss along with electromagnetic waves of 9.4 gigahertz and 17 megahertz, the mice did not die and were never sensitive to another infection. Rabbits were also infected with a usually fatal bacteria, but lived because of the same treatment.

The part played by the high frequency radio waves is unclear, however the body reacts to both electricity and magnetism and probably hundreds of particular radio waves. This study opens up even more areas of investigation.

These studies suggest that magnetic treatments might have great potential for prevention of other ailments. Dr. Kyoichi Nakagawa, a physician in Japan pointed out that Earth's magnetic field has decreased nearly 50% over the past 500 years. This, combined with the time people now spend in cars and concrete buildings and airplanes results in what he called a "magnetic field deficiency syndrome", and suggested that it could account for a number of subclinical symptoms such as poor sleeping, feelings of mild depression, fatigue, increased frequency of minor ailments, etc. His research led him to develop the magnetic sleeping system (described in Chapter VI) designed to supplement the body's magnetic deficiency. Hundreds of thousands of people have apparently benefited from this device and one of its biggest values may be in the prevention of many ailments, although this is a difficult thing to measure.

Calcium ion movements are affected by magnetic fields (see Chapter VII) and this may be why old injuries so often respond to PMF. While working at the Manomet Medical Clinic in Plymouth, Massachusetts, the author treated a woman who had broken both feet in an automobile accident. She had been in pain for four years and unable to walk easily. After only four hours total of treatment with pulsed magnetic fields, spread out over two weeks, she was not only able to walk easily, but even to dance! She was delighted.

A surfer with a broken leg treated it with the PULSAR (thru the cast) for one hour a day for two weeks, and then took the cast off and went surfing. His doctor had said healing would take four weeks and surfing wouldn't be possible that season.

A skier injured his thumb tendon, had surgery, and was experiencing pain and stiffness in it. Four daily treatments dramatically improved the motility.

In the case of broken bones, more calcium ions need to be deposited, but in the case of arthritis, it's desirable to have calcium migrate away from the joints, therefore treatment with the opposite polarity is called for. A woman who came into the clinic in Plymouth with such painful arthritis that she had to walk with a cane, was pain free and cane free after seven hours of treatment distributed over a three week period.

These cases are typical of the power of magnetic fields to stimulate the body's natural healing processes.

A more formal study on arthritis was reported at the Madras conference. Patients with arthritis, spondylosis, and malunion of fractures were treated with pulsed magnetic fields from .01 to 1 hz. The polarity and strength was not specified. About 80-85% of the patients recovered (total number not specified) and recurrence occurred in only two patients after a two year period.

Brain injuries are another topic reported on at the Madras conference. One hundred cases were divided into two groups: one received PMF and they showed improvement by clinical assessment as well as by CT scans. The treatments appeared to increase sodium ion flow, reduce swelling, and speed tissue repair.

While having dinner with a friend, his wife said she had a terrible headache and would have to cancel the class she had planned to teach. After fifteen minutes of treatment with the north pole of the PULSAR her headache was completely gone. She taught her class, returned at midnite to chat with us, and was up early the next morning with no trace of a headache.

A house guest said she had migraine and there were spots of light in front of her eyes. After about four minutes of treatment with the north polarity she said: "I can see out of one eye now." Four minutes later the other eye cleared up and she was symptom free during the rest of her visit.

A newspaper reporter came by to obtain information about magnetic field treatments and aging. The PULSAR definitely helps older people become more energetic and there are various anecdotal reports on white hair turning black again, mice living longer, or sex drive returning. The reporter happened to mention she had premenstrual cramps and while we were talking she applied the north polarity to her abdomen. Within 7 minutes she was free of painful cramps. This was typical of every woman with menstrual cramps who has used it.

In another person a leg cramp was almost instantly relieved, a child with growing pains received quick relief, a friend who sprained his thumb overdoing carpentry obtained relief in about 15 minutes and two conditions of extreme fatigue vanished within about 15 minutes of treatment.

An associate who has been using the magnetic sleeping system for two years said she has only lost her temper once during that time. Such effects are typical of perhaps several hundred similar ones in the author's experience.

Of course magnetic fields don't "heal" anything; they only help the body heal itself. And they don't always help everything heal either. Magnetic field treatments are not a substitute for medical treatments, they are an adjunct and may be used in conjunction with any other dietary, chemical, or physical treatment.

Although magnetic treatments alone can often do wonders to help the body heal itself, it's always worthwhile to take advantage of all the wonderful knowledge available to speed up the healing process. Sometimes magnetic treatments can only start the healing process—other health practices are necessary to keep it going. Almost everyone's diet can be improved or altered to help heal some specific disease or condition. Knowledge is now commonly available on what specific vitamins or minerals will help what types of ailments. Herbs and homeopathic remedies are also helpful for many conditions.

Exercise of the appropriate type is usually one of the most helpful healing remedies, especially if it includes deep breathing, sunshine, and immersion in the ocean. A unique exercise program has been developed by the author which is designed to introduce variety into an exercise routine.* Maintaining a positive mental attitude helps, whatever the treatment procedure. Since a placebo effect is known to exist for practically every kind of health treatment, one might as well expect the best and enlist the power of the mind as much as possible in the healing process.

---

* Called the PSYCHOENERGETICS FITNESS DECK, it is available from PsychoPhysics Labs. The fitness deck consists of 52 cards, each with an illustrated exercise. To use it, one shuffles the deck and draws 4 or more cards for one's daily program. There is always an element of suprise, for there are over 100,000 possible four card combinations!

The author has been a professional hypnotist for many years and knows and appreciates the power of thought to heal, especially when proper- ly focused.* Hypnosis, meditation, affirmations, positive suggestions, focused prayers, or even just deep relaxation can be helpful. A previous book: BIOMEDITATION, has been written on this subject (see Chapter XI), and a biofeedback instrument designed and patented by the author is now available from Radio Shack at low cost to help people learn deep relaxation as a prerequisite for self hypnosis. In a way, hypnosis is akin to magnetization of a material, for hypnosis consists of aligning the mind, body, and emotions in order to achieve some focused purpose. To magnetize a material some of the electron spins, the little crystalline-like chunks called domains, and perhaps even some of the nuclear spins, can

---

*Thought combined with emotion may alter the biofield as described in Chapter III. The thoughts of several million people, if properly focused and organized, apparently can affect, not only the entire field of the Earth, but even the Sun's activity. This incredible statement is supported by experimental evidence. The academy for Peace Research carried out a 3 1/2 year study correlating solar activity dips with global peace meditations. There is apparently some link between magnetism, thought, the Biofield, and the activity of the Sun. (see Sources-Chapter XI).

all be aligned. It's interesting that Mesmer did both hypnosis and magnetic treatments with his patients. This is one of the many possible future applications which will be discussed in the next chapter.

CHAPTER VIII

PRINCIPLES OF
MAGNETIC FIELD TREATMENT

Where to Treat

The first place to treat is obviously the site of the injury or where there is pain, tightness, or feeling of constriction. Or, if you know by magnetic diagnosis or other means, treat any gland or organ that is out of balance. If the condition is general, such as depression, weakness, or anxiety, treat the chest area or up and down the spine. Since magnetic fields penetrate most materials, you can place magnets over clothing, as long as the applicator is within a quarter inch of the body.

Secondary treatment sites are glands which might be related to an injury or illness, or organs which have connections with the problem as described in Chinese medicine. Acupuncture points along relevant meridans or reflex points in the feet may be treated if they are known or can be found.

For back injuries the applicator may be placed up and down the spine and even at the top of the head. In general, any place that is sore to the touch may be treated.

Proper balance of the hormone system is fundamental to good health and the glandular secretions interconnect in complex ways. While treating one particular gland or organ may help, and probably won't hurt, you may need to know the full pattern to provide effective therapy. More details are provided in the book: ENERGY THERAPY by Drs. Mary and Richard Broeringmeyer (see Sources, Chapter XI).

Which Polarity to Use

If you use a muscle test for diagnosis, then treat with the magnetic polarity which makes the muscle stronger.

In general, if a person has a recent injury which is painful or inflamed, treat with the north pole until the pain and inflammation subsides.

Chronic muscular or joint conditions usually need south pole fields to stimulate healing. Chronic soreness around glands or organs (see Chapter V for illustrations of their location) may need either north or south polarity, depending on whether or not the organ or gland is hypo or hyper active. If you know the gland or organ is underactive, treat with the south polarity. A muscle test can still be useful to confirm the presumed polarity.

The north pole relaxes, reduces, makes more alkaline, sedates, or calms biological activity. The south pole stimulates, acidifies, tonifies, increases growth, or strengthens biological activity. Therefore do not use the south pole on an infection. The harmful bacteria present will be stimulated to increase. Treat an infection with north pole magnetism. Headaches, colds, sore throats, tightness in the chest, stiff necks, sore muscles, stomach cramps, or premenstrual symptoms usually require north pole energies.

DO NOT TREAT TUMORS, CANCEROUS CONDITIONS, OR INFECTIONS WITH BIOMAGNETIC SOUTH POLE FIELDS.

In general, if any other minor condition worsens after a few minutes treatment, reverse the polarity.

If a condition worsens when either polarity is applied, better not treat with magnetism. The following chart summarizes the different effects of north and south poles:

SOUTH POLE	NORTH POLE
Increases hydrogen ions (acidity)	Decreases hydrogen ions
Stimulates all forms of life	Decreases pain
Increases protein activity	Decreases calcium ions
Softens & expands capillary canals	Decreases protein activity
Helps the production of red blood cells	Decreases inflammation
Increases digestion	Decreases glandular activity
Disperses body fluids	Decreases organ activity
Vaso-dilates	Vaso-constricts
Stimulates glandular function	Reduces cholestrol build-up
Stimulates organ functions	Sedating, calming
Increases seed yield	Dissolves fatty tissue

What to Treat

Because magnetic fields work at the subatomic level as well as the ionic, they are effective for a wide variety of diseases and conditions. Anything may be treated of course. It will either respond or it won't. There are no harmful side effects except for those already noted in the case of tumors, cancers, or infections. Those should be treated only with north magnetic fields. Over treatment does not necessarily help one become super healthy. Healing takes time, no matter what the treatment.

For the average common minor ailment, it is the author's experience, and that of Dr. Larry Price, a physician who used a PULSAR in a walk-in clinic, on Cape Code that magnetic field therapy will help about 70-80% of the time.

Emotional upsets can also be treated by magnetic field therapy. If someone is sad, upset, anxious, nervous, tense, or stressed, apply the north pole over the chest area. If possible do a complete diagnosis, for emotional states are related to glandular conditons as well as physical, dietary, or psychological ones.

If someone is tired, depressed, or weak, apply the south pole of the PULSAR to the chest area, throat, or around the eyes and forehead. Don't overstimulate. Don't apply high gauss magnetic fields to the head area: this can cause mild headaches.

Ultimately the person being treated must decide whether or not a treatment or polarity is helping. Always give the person the respect of being able to tune into the wisdom of their own body and choose what is right for them.

If someone experiences a slight increase in pain, stiffness, or discomfort, then the polarity is probably incorrect, or the strength may be too large, or the frequency or waveform may be wrong.

How Long To Treat

Treatment times of 15 to 30 minutes twice a day are sufficient for most conditions. Greater magnetic strength or longer treatment times are not necessarily better, although they won't be harmful. For chronic conditions, five or six treatments may be necessary before any improvement is noted. If any improvement at all occurs, more may be expected with continued treatment. If no improvement is observed after five or six days, then magnetic field treatments probably won't help that particular condition.

Before each succeeding treatment, muscle test to ascertain polarity needed for the condition. A person can change on different days and may need different polarities. This may be due to changes in Earth's magnetic field, changes in the body, the psychology, or combinations of these.

What to Expect

It is often said that a condition has to get worse before it gets better. The patient is supposed to experience a healing crisis, a worsening of the symptoms, or an outpouring of the condition. While this may happen with other forms of treatment, it is not the author's experience with magnetotherapy. If magnetic treatments are going to help at all, only improvement takes place, not a worsening of the condition.

About 90% of the women who have an acute injury will feel a slight tingling or pulsating sensation when pulsed magnetic fields are applied. The sensation will sometimes be noticed throughout the body, perhaps along an acupuncture meridan or some nerve pathway. Only about 1% of the men who have an acute injury will feel any kind of sensation. Generally people who have chronic injuries feel nothing, though women are more apt to experience a sensation than men. If people feel something from the PULSAR it is almost certainly going to be helpful. And it may be helpful, even if nothing is felt. Long ago Mesmer noticed that people who are ill sometimes see a faint glow around a magnet in a completely dark room, but healthy people see nothing.

******

In summary, magnetic treatments are simple, rapid, inexpensive, and free from adverse side effects. There are no medicines, injections, salves, or electrodes to be applied to the skin to frighten the patient. Within a few days of successive treatments, even the most severe conditions may show an improvement. Minor conditions often improve within minutes.

As the science of magnetic healing develops, it promises to be a tremendous help to all humanity.

Some of the scientific basis for exactly how magnetic fields promote healing will be discussed in the next chapter. Research is going on in many laboratories around the world and international conferences on the subject are a yearly occurrence.

CHAPTER IX

HOW DO MAGNETIC FIELDS HEAL?

Until recently this was a scientific mystery, and ignorance of mechanisms mistakenly kept magnetic healing in the realm of quackery. Now the mystery is being rapidly resolved as researcher after researcher each uncovers another piece of supporting evidence. Gradually, but surely, theories and predictive techniques are being built up on a solid foundation which is likely to produce a revolution in medicine in the next decade.

Some of these studies are discussed in the following pages. In some   cases, there is good, solid, practically irrefutable, experimental data; in others there are grayer areas of formal and informal observations, personal experience, reasonable speculations and inferences, and even loose suppositions and wild conjectures.   It's important to note more than just the narrow and solid 'truth', because today's anecdotal reports often are the sparks for next year's research studies. Our ignorance in this area is so vast that practically any thoughtful experiment using magnetic fields is likely to uncover something new. It's definitely a realm for the scientific explorer.

How magnetic fields promote healing does not have a simple answer. Magnetic fields operate at different structural or physical size levels. The largest level is perhaps the whole body field or biofield as described in Chapter III. Below that in size are the circulatory and nervous systems of the body, then individual organs, muscles, glands, cells, molecules, ions, atoms, and tiniest of all, sub-atomic or elementary particles—electrons and protons. Although one could argue that since everything is made up of electrons and protons and a few other elementary particles, only magnetic interactions with these particles is of importance. However, different experimenters have focused their research on different levels and on specifically organized structures, so it's appropriate to look at what has been done without attempting to break it down to magnetic effects on electrons and protons. Therefore we will discuss each structural level in turn.

Biofield Changes

The author observed a difference in biofield activity before and after treatment with pulsed magnetic fields. After treatment, the amplitude of the biofield is reduced. This corresponds to a more relaxed state. This is only a casual observation and a more formal study could be done. It is supported by the observation of Dr. Laurence Badgley who discovered a different way to detect the presence of a similar, but possibly related biofield around the body using crystals and blood pulse amplitude changes observed at the wrist. If there is an injury or disease localized at some place in the body, Badgley found he could detect a local spiral vortex pattern at that place by changes in the pulse amplitude observed when a crystal was passed thru the field boundary. After treatment with pulsed magnetic fields or some other healing remedy, the local disturbance in the energy field disappears.

These observations suggest that the biofield around the body may interact directly with magnetic field treatments. When the biofield is smoothed out or restored to normal, it may in turn influence the body chemistry to help healing occur. Applying magnetic fields may be a kind of 'massage' of the biofield. Mesmer and other healers achieved this by stroking the body's 'aura' with magnets. Mesmer later found that he could produce a similar effect by using his hands instead of magnets. This ties in with the author's observations that the biofield can easily be detected around the hands as described in Chapter III.

Organs

Evidence for producing an effect in an organ such as the colon, liver, or stomach is observational and anecdotal. At least the author knows of no formal studies that have been undertaken to measure functioning at this level. If a person is aware of a feeling of pain or constriction in an organ, and/or if testing of any muscle for strength shows a difference when north or south polarity is applied to that organ, then treatment with magnetism will usually make a noticeable difference. The person will usually report that he or she feels better, feels a relaxation of tightness in the area, or feels stimulated.

For instance, bowel movements often occur immediately after treating a tight colon. Premenstrual cramps are usually relieved in minutes by application of the north magnetic pole.

Bones

In one experiment on mice, leg bones were weighed and measured after treatment and showed 4-11% greater weight and 4-9% greater lengths than a group of controls. The treatment procedure consisted of applying a 10,000 gauss permanent magnetic field for a 30 minute period each day for ten days. Polarity was not mentioned in the abstract of the report, so probably both a north and south pole field was used. It's likely that the results would have been greater if only the south pole had been used, and if a pulsing field had been used rather than a permanent field.

Bassett has done considerable research on healing of fractures with pulsed magnetic fields. He maintains that tiny electric currents generated by the applied magnetic fields affect cells which in turn result in calcification of the fibrocartilage in the gap in the bone fracture. Then bone cells grow on the calcified fibrocartilage until the bone is healed. However there may be

other mechanisms of healing besides those produced by generation of electric currents. (See the
section on calcium for more information.) A permanent magnet would not generate any significant electric current compared to a pulsed field
and the nature of the current so generated would
be different, yet, as previously mentioned, permanent magnets do work.

Blood Flow and Oxygen Content

In one study, (polarity unstated) pulsed magnetic fields of about 10 hz were applied to the
head area. Infrared monitoring showed that the
temperature of the hands and arms increased,
indicating increased blood flow (Warnke).

People using the PULSAR often report a sensation of heat at the site of treatment. Apparently
the capillaries and blood vessels dilate due to the
presence of a pulsed magnetic field.

Dr. Benjamin Lau applied a magnetic field
pulsed at 12 to 20 hz of 5 gauss intensity to the
heart region. Significant increases in blood flow
were found in 90% of the subjects. Sixty per cent
of the subjects showed blood flow increases two
to four times above their initial values. Since the

polarity was unstated, he probably used alternating fields.

Both Dr. Lau, and Dr. Warnke in Europe did experiments showing that the oxygen in blood or tissues increased dramatically after treatment with pulsed magnetic fields. Dr. Lau observed an increase in oxygen partial pressure up to four times normal in 90% of the subjects. Dr. Warnke found an average increase of 200% in his subjects. In Canada, pulsed magnetic field instruments are used on horses. In one experiment it was found that treatment increased oxygen blood volume by 52%!

One of the most delightful findings by the author was a complete absence of high altitude breathing difficulty when going from sea level to 14,000 feet. The south pole of a PULSAR was applied to the heart only for a few days for about 30 minutes each day prior to the skiing or hiking trips. Professional athletes are beginning to discover this valuable result of magnetic field treatments.

Since the blood carries oxygen to cells, it seems reasonable that more oxygen would result in faster or more complete metabolism for healing injured tissues. The blood leucocycte count is reported to be influenced by magnetic fields according to V. Beasley. He is also one of several people who have claimed that red blood cells seen in a microscope will line up when a magnetic field is applied. The author has tried this experiment but has not seen any such effect from use of the PULSAR or permanent magnetic fields of several hundred gauss.

Exactly how magnetic fields affect blood circulation is still a mystery.

Hormones

Davis reported that mice and other animals showed increased sexual activity when the south pole of a permanent magnet was applied to the ovaries or gonads. He also reported that this led to premature aging. The author observed that pulsed fields could stimulate the sex desire via a link from the pituitary region to the thyroid and then to the gonads.

OMNI writer Kathleen McAuliffe reported that a West German researcher found the pineal gland sensitive to magnetic fields. Broeringmeyer has long maintained that all glands can be stimulated or depressed in their activity, depending on the polarity of the magnetic field.

For example, a woman came into the author's office with diabetes as diagnosed by hospital tests. A magnetic diagnosis showed a hyperactive adrenal gland. Of the many hormones secreted by the adrenals, one inhibits the activity of the pancreas and reduces the amount of insulin. She treated herself by applying the north polarity side of the applicator from the PULSAR to the overactive adrenal for a few days. Her blood sugar dropped and she was able to reduce the amount of insulin she had been taking.

Exactly how magnetic fields stimulate or calm down glandular activity is a mystery. Possibly it may be the direction of a spin field, hypothesized to exist around glands, which is either increased by one polarity or counteracted by the other polarity. Both permanent and pulsed magnetic fields operate to increase or slow down glandular activity.

Cells

A primary cause of some diseases is now attributed to malfunction of certain types of tissue cells in the body. A change in the voltage across the cell membrane occurs when the body is ill. This contributes to the slowing down of the metabolism, with subsequent reduction in oxygen utilization efficiency. Pulsed magnetic field therapy, as compared with a constant magnetic field, produces a pulse of very low electric current within the fluids of the body. This could (speculates one writer) facilitate ionic transfer across the cell membrane. It's very difficult to observe exactly what's going on within a living cell. Researchers have to resort to indirect methods of observation and make reasonable inferences.

Cell division rate can be altered by magnetic fields. Jose Delagado, a Spanish physician who has extensively investigated magnetic field therapies, wrote: "There's no doubt that electromagnetic fields alter the mitotic index of cells— even weak fields have powerful effects.

A French physician, M. Barnotly, also observed that magnetic fields could modify the normal rate of cell division and he thought they could also alter the stability of the genetic code.

Water

Water has long been known to be affected by magnetic fields. Water from underground sources often contains dissolved calcium and other minerals and pollutants which are harmful to users in various ways. In industrial uses requiring hot water, any dissolved calcium precipitates out as a scale on the inside of pipes. This scale can eventually clog the pipes, akin to cholestrol plating out on the blood vessel walls. This is costly to remove. Water treatment, usually by permanent magnets, can significantly reduce the surface tension of water and increase the pH (make it less acidic). Treated water greatly reduces pipe scaling. (Magnetic treatments have also been reported to reduce cholestrol levels, although the mechanism is probably different.)

Plant growth, too, is reported to be accelerated by watering the plants with magnetically treated (south pole) water. The author has no personal experience with this. It seems like it would be hard to prove considering the variety of other factors that enter into plant growth such as soil conditions, potential interactive effects with the experimenter, difficulty of maintaining adequate controls, and intrinsic individual plant variations. Yet so many researchers have reported positive results that it merits a thorough investigation.

The experiment on altering the taste of wine described in Chapter V supports the notion that the pH of water can be altered, as do many other observations. Water molecules are known to have a small interaction with magnetic fields and some researchers have theorized that water molecules sometimes form in very long chains. Perhaps magnetic fields can influence this chain formation and consequently alter the biochemistry involving water in the body. It may be that the formation of long chains is what is observed as surface tension changes of water due to the treatment with magnetic fields.

Enzymes

Enzymes are biological catalysts which help many chemical reactions within the body occur more thoroughly or more quickly. Biological enzymes are different than catalysts used in the laboratory or in industry because they break down during use and have to be replenished by intake of food or rebuilt by the body.   Enzyme failure is significant in many diseases.

Basset reports that enzyme action is enhanced by pulsed magnetic fields, although he doesn't say which enzymes and what experiments were performed. Adenomonophosphate (AMP) ions, which transfer enzymatic action within the cell, become more active under the influence of magnetic fields according to other researchers.

A quantitative study on the enzyme Trypsin was done by Smith and Cook. They measured chemical reactions which took place between the north and south poles of a 5,000 gauss permanent magnet and found that the enzyme activity increased. They thought that the magnetic fields helped the complex enzyme molecules to stay organized rather than breaking apart as is usually the case after a few hours of activity.

Resonance and Entrainment

All bodies have unique acoustic and mechanical resonant frequencies which are a function of their size and shape. Living organisms or cells, tissues, and organs within organisms, also may have electromagnetic resonant frequencies which are a function of their intrinsic electrical activity. For example, the heart beat is a very large electrical pulse (and very minute magnetic pulse) varying between one and two cycles per second. The brain cells operate at frequencies between 3 and 30 cycles per second, with peak activity centering around 10-16 cycles.

These frequencies, therefore, are obvious ones to use in magnetic field treatments because they will entrain or help the body vibrate at its natural rhythms. It's desirable that the applied field frequencies be in phase with the body's phase. Dr. Laurence Badgley's unique instrument applies a pulsed field which is snychronized with the patients heartbeat.*

Other researchers have experimented with repetition pulses or frequencies on the order of predominant brain wave frequencies such as 10 hz,

---

*PsychoPhysics Labs has developed an instrument which helps two people synchronize their heartbeats with each other. This, along with practice in breath-heartbeat synchronization produces inter and intra harmony that is profoundly relaxing and beneficial.

the alpha frequency, or 7.8 hz, the Schuman resonance. The Schuman resonance has taken on a magical-mystical connotation by some writers, but it is simply the speed of light divided by the circumference of the Earth. It's not a very precise number and it's use in magnetic or electric therapy has not shown it to be particularly significant in the author's experience or that of Dr. Badgley. Of course, magnetic fields do interact with brain waves, and people have even succeeded in inducing visual images directly in the brain with the proper electromagnetic pulses. This is an open area for further research.

Complex Molecules

Atoms consist of a single nucleus surrounded by a cloud of electrons. Molecules consist of two or more atoms united by sharing one or more electrons. Some molecules used by the body consist of thousands of individual atoms bound together.

Even though most atoms have net magnetic fields arising from their constitutent sub-atomic particles, when they are combined to form molecules they are usually so oriented that the magnetic field of one atom cancels out the magnetic field of an adjacent atom. Two exceptions are nitric oxide and oxygen gas. Each of these molecules acts like a little magnet. Dissolved oxygen is present in the blood and tissues. Applying a pulsed magnetic field to the chest region helps increase oxygen utilization, but how this occurs is unknown at the present time.

In 1966, a researcher, M. Labes, proposed that liquid crystals could be one way in which biological systems respond to magnetic fields. Liquid crystals are rod-like molecules or clusters of such molecules, some of whose properties are altered by magnetic fields. Complex lipids, or liquid crystals, are present in the adrenal cortex, ovaries, and myelin, a substance found around nerves.

Proteoglycans and collagens, building block molecules of cartilage, are also affected in a positive way by magnetic fields. Colloidal suspensions, key aspects of human biochemistry, are definitely changed by magnetic fields. Probably hundreds of biochemical or organic reactions are influenced by magnetic fields of the proper pattern and amplitude.

Calcium Ions

Calcium ions play a vital role in biological activity. Researchers such as W. Ross Adey at the Veterans Hospital in Loma Linda, California have found that magnetic fields produced in the laboratory, as well as fluctuations in Earth's magnetic field, can alter calcium ion activity in cells and nerves.

A 16 hz field was found by Blackman and other researchers to increase the flow of calcium ions in the brain tissue of chickens. Calcium, sodium, potassium and magnesium ions can all be influenced by pulsed magnetic fields in the frequency range between 10 and 100 cycles per second. (Surgalla has written research and review papers —see references.) When fields alter the way calcium is attached to cell membranes, a chemical domino effect that starts on the surface may spread to the heart of the cell and could even influence the genetic code according to Blackman.

Calcium ions can be helped to migrate to bone

surfaces to help fractures heal in half the time (Bassett), or they can help calcium ions move away from arthritic joints (Lau). These researchers did not mention polarity, however. Broeringmeyer has found that this is an important variable for permanent magnets and the author has also found it significant when pulsed magnetic fields are used.

Hydrogen Ions

The late Dr. Ralph Sierra, one of the major contributors to magnetic healing techniques, maintained that the hydrogen proton was altered by magnetic fields. Broeringmeyer and Davis also stressed the importance of magnetic fields on hydrogen ions. They observed that the south pole of a magnet produced more hydrogen ions in ionic solutions, thereby increasing acidity, and north pole fields shifted ionic fluids to a more alkaline state. Although the author knows of no formal study on this observation, the reader can easily demonstrate its validity (see experiment 2, Chapter V). This is a fundamental discovery since the acid-base balance is carefully maintained in the blood, organs, and tissues of the body, and if it varies one way or the other different types of disease can manifest from tooth decay to cancer. (Perhaps some reader with a sensitive pH meter will undertake a more formal study.)

Perhaps a clue as to how this happens is provided by a recent Scientific American article (April, 1988) by Laloe and Freed. They describe experiments on spin polarizing hydrogen atoms to alter their chemical properties.

Hydrogen atoms are made up of a nucleus (a particle called a proton) and a single electron moving around the proton. Both the electron and the proton possess the property called spin (see chapter II), and are observed to interact with magnetic fields. Usually hydrogen atoms, if left alone, quickly combine to form hydrogen molecules, composed of two hydrogen atoms, but if the hydrogen atoms have their electrons spin polarized, that is aligned in the same directions, then the hydrogen atoms avoid each other and therefore don't combine to form hydrogen molecules. This leaves them free to become hydrogen ions. This behavior is described by the Pauli exclusion principle of quantum mechanics, which basically says that identical objects can't be in the same place at the same time, and consequently the two electrons of the hydrogen atoms won't combine to share a common space around the two atoms—a necessary condition to form the molecule.

This is easier to visualize if you imagine that the electrons are not solid little spinning tops, but act more like spinning clouds. When they are by themselves they may act more like spherical clouds, but when they are connected with a proton, as in the hydrogen atom, they are more like a spinning doughnut shaped cloud which surrounds the entire proton. In the case of the atom, which consists of two protons and two electrons, the two clouds must combine in some manner to form a common cloud around both protons. Freed and Laloe found that if the single electron clouds around single atoms are magnetized, or spin polarized, the clouds won't combine with one another to form a double cloud, so hydrogen gas won't form.

Another way of picturing this is to imagine that the hydrogen atoms with their electron clouds are like little magnetic spheres with either a north pole facing outward in all directions or a south pole facing outward in all directions.

Normally there would be an even mixture of north out and south out atoms and they would easily find their opposites and clump together to form hydrogen molecules. But if more of the atomic spheres are spin polarized or magnetized so only one polarity is facing outwards, those polarized atoms would repel one another and therefore stay as separate atoms rather than combine to form molecular hydrogen.

Laloe and Freed performed their experiments on gases at very low temperatures, in order to slow down the random kinetic motions of the atoms due to what we call heat, and bring out the effect of interest. They did not mention magnetic polarity in their report and they apparently used a traditional magnetic field consisting of north pole on one side of the reactive chamber and south pole on the other side. They might have obtained different results if they had explored the effects of different polarities.

Based on their work, what can we say about the behavior of hydrogen ions in solutions?   In a liquid the hydrogen ions are slowed down, perhaps like low temperature slows down the hydrogen atoms in a gas. In the case of hydrogen ions, we are only dealing with the hydrogen protons, not the electrons. The protons, too, are considered to be like little spinning tops and are observed to change their spin direction in an external magnetic field, showing the link between spin and magnetism discussed in Chapter III.

In ordinary neutral water there are always a small number of hydrogen ions (positive) and an equal number of hydroxyl (OH-negative) ions. Overall they balance out leaving a pH of 7 or neutral condition. If an external magnetic field is capable of spin polarizing some of the hydrogen nuclei or ions, then one direction of polarity could result in preventing them from recombining with OH ions to form water. Whereas, spin polarizing in the other direction could result in more hydrogens getting together to form neutral water. This model would indicate that magnetic fields could not make water alkaline, but could make it more or less acidic. That is, it could only move to one side of a neutral pH - the acid side. However what spin polarization could do to the OH ion is unknown. Some careful experimentation is needed in this area.

Perhaps the effects of magnetic fields on other chemical reactions are also due to effects on hydrogen ions and the acid-base balance of the solutions in which the other chemical reactions are observed.

In living organisms, water is often organized in almost crystalline-like forms, known as living water or bio-water by biologists. It is different from ordinary free water—in fact water is quite an extraordinary substance. In an organism, the living water may be organized in some manner similar to that produced by extremely low temperatures or by magnetic fields. Under such conditions, small external magnetic fields, such as those applied artificially or those which occur as Earth's magnetic field changes, could have significant effects. By means of quantum effects, changes in the spin of hydrogen protons, can produce the macroscopic chemical, physiological, cellular, or behavioral changes which are in fact observed. The living organism is a sensitive high gain amplifier of energy units on the order of a few quantums.

Chemical Bonds and Quantum Physics

Besides hydrogen protons, carbon and phosphorus and many other atomic nuclei play important parts in body chemistry. These atomic nuclei are like little spinning tops, and like tops, when they are knocked or hit a rough spot on the floor, they can wobble erratically. In the presence of an external magnetic field, these nuclei can straighten up and realign the way they are supposed to be. Although the image of a spinning top is hardly accurate, it does give a picture we can relate to. Both the atomic nuclei and the outer electron spins can be altered by magnetic fields. As in the case of hydrogen protons and atoms, chemical reactions that involve these elements too can be altered by magnetic fields.

Magnetic Resonance Imaging

Research on magnetic resonance imaging has turned up another clue as to why magnetic fields help the body heal. In MRI a strong magnetic field is applied to the body which aligns the spins of atomic nuclei. Then a radio wave of a specific frequency is directed at those spin aligned nuclei which knocks them out of alignment by a slight amount, causing them to wobble or precess. They usually come quickly back to their initial alignment position and in the process of doing so they send out a radio wave signal which is computer processed to develop a picture used by the MRI technician to diagnose the condition of the body.

Depending on the condition of the person, and the strength, direction, and polarity of the MRI field, the individual could be helped, or hindered in the healing process. A report in Science News for June 19, 1988 is most relevant for this topic. Ian Smith, a Canadian scientist found, that if people had cancer, and had an MRI diagnosis, and if the nuclei were slow to recover after being kicked out of alignment by a radio wave, then that cancer would be more likely to spread.

This important observation supports the finding that cancer is helped to heal by appropriate magnetic field treatment, and suggests that one of the mechanisms of healing lies in proper realigning of the spins of atomic nuclei.

The application of a radio wave to disturb the spins seems like it would be detrimental to the body. The author has talked with two people who reported unpleasant feelings after MRI, but has not made any kind of study of people who have received this treatment. It would seem that it would be important to consider the principles discussed in this book and apply a final magnetic field of a particular type that would help realign any nuclear spins disturbed by the radio waves. This might be different in each case.

******

This completes our discussion of the many ways in which magnetic fields help the body heal. It may be that there is only one fundamental principle involved—the realignment of electron or nuclear spins, but this seems too simplistic. As has so often been written in this book: "More research needs to be done." Perhaps you will be the one to do it.

CHAPTER X

THE FUTURE OF
MAGNETIC HEALING

Although this is the shortest chapter in the book, it's potentially the longest, for what we now know about magnetic healing is practically nothing compared with what we will eventually learn. Magnetism will play an even larger part in our lives in the future. From health improvement to food treatment, from interpersonal behavior to social behavior, life is highly influenced by magnetic fields; and when we understand more about the principles and mechanisms, we will increase our power and free will to make our own choices. Magnetic forces may help humankind get to the stars by preserving and healing the body in long flights, or perhaps by contributing to the means of operating interstellar drives.

Disease Healing, Especially Cancer

As people learn more about the precise ways in which magnetic fields can help the healing process, more and more ailments will be successfully treated. Future treatment devices will probably be whole body systems which a person will lie on, or slide into like big cages. Computer aided diagnosis and controlled precision treatments will be given to realign particular glands, organs, or areas of the body. Perhaps regular magnetic "tune-ups" will be as common as car check ups or teeth cleaning is now.

Cancer is a prime candidate for effective treatment by properly designed and applied magnetic fields. When cancer occurs in the body, there is an interference with cell division and growth. Magnetic field treatments have already been shown to have some beneficial results on cancer; the exact mechanisms of healing are not yet known and therefore, results are probably less than what they could be.

So far we have two clues to aid our understanding: 1) It has been observed that the rate of cell division is altered by magnetic fields, so there is some link with the cell growth process, and

2) Magnetic Resonance Imaging observations on people with cancer show delayed relaxation times of nuclei (described in Chapter IX).

Careful research will probably soon uncover precisely what waveforms, pulse rates, field strengths, and/or adjunctive radio frequencies will restore cell functioning to its healthy mode. Perhaps each disease, or each organ will need to be treated with different electromagnetic patterns.

Another disease of importance is AIDS. Studies should be undertaken at once with AIDS patients. Magnetic fields are known to affect the thymus gland which is important in the operation of the immune system and this gland can probably be strengthened by periodic treatments.

Of course, as is the case with so many ailments, prevention may be the best course of action. Regular magnetic treatments may be as routine as vaccinations are today. In the future each child may be 'magnetically' innoculated against different diseases.

Naturally it will still be necessary to pay attention to proper diet, stress reactions, or psychological considerations. If a person wants to be ill, the power of thought will over ride any physical-magnetic realignment of the body, or he or she will simply refuse treatment. On the other hand, it's a lot easier to think positive thoughts if one is free of pain or sickness.

Dioxin, DDT, etc.

These chemicals and others are being widely dispersed in the environment and then recon-centrated in food chains. Individuals differ in their sensitivity to these toxins, and possibly those people who are most susceptible would be strengthened in their resistance by appropriate magnetic field treatments. Research needs to be done—any positive effects at all would be helpful. In the future, perhaps magnetic fields could be used to pluck these toxins right out of the body or transform them into harmless compounds by somehow interacting directly and specifically with the molecules.

Limb Regeneration and Wound Healing

Every cell in the body carries two copies of the genetic code which is the blueprint for that individual. Minute electric currents have been found to help limb regeneration in some animals. How and why does it work?—We don't know. Is the original blueprint for growth being accessed and restimulated by electric currents? Magnetic fields can induce tiny currents inside living cells where it would be impossible to place electrodes. Perhaps it will be possible to reactivate the basic growth switch for wound healing and limb regeneration. At the present time we don't know the code, but new and more powerful techniques for looking inside the cell are continually being developed. A photograph of DNA showing the coiled form of the molecule was just obtained in 1988. Direct alteration of DNA and RNA is already being done with lasers. Magnetic fields may help in this process .

Mental Illness

There are many types and causes of mental illness: genetic, hormonal, dietary, psychological and social factors all play a part. The more complex a system, the more ways it can malfunction. Nevertheless, magnetic influences definitely are a significant factor in mental illness. In Chapter IV evidence was presented indicating that geomagnetic storms are triggers for episodes of psychosis. At least two seperate studies were done in different countries and the records of thousands of patients with mental illness were examined. If some types of magnetic fields adversely affect people, then other types are likely to have beneficial effects. Indeed, some schizophrenic conditions are reported to have been helped by simple application of permanent magnets. Several hundred years ago Mesmer noticed that magnets help mental illness.

Scientists in the Soviet Union have already tried shielding sensitive people from the effects of geomagnetic storms, but they didn't use the proper magnetic shielding; they only used shielding for radio waves. More effective shielding might help some people remain calm and stable, but who wants to walk around in a Mu metal box (Mu metal is a special metal used for magnetic shielding—see Magnetic Helmets in Sources, Chapter XI). Remedial magnetic field treatments might offset disruptive geomagnetic disturbances and literally help them "straighten out their heads". It's quite likely that hormonal imbalances associated with mental illness could be corrected by magnetic field treatments.

Planetary Magnetism

The geomagnetic disturbances which upset some people are often associated with planetary positions. When people understand more about the different types of magnetic field patterns which come and go in Earth's field, we will be able to pinpoint specific patterns related to specific celestial events. The data is already available and just needs careful analysis. Some geomagnetic patterns are beneficial or stimulating to humans. If each planet has its own characteristic magnetic pattern, as the data now suggests, then it may be possible to artificially duplicate the pattern, simply by recording it and sending it back into an applicator like those used in the PULSAR instruments. Different planetary patterns will probably have different usages. Different people probably will need different patterns just as some people need different vitamins or minerals.

Sleep Learning

Direct transmission of mental images by electro-magnetic means has already been achieved by Dr. Elizabeth Rauscher and others. Direct encoding of significant information may be possible in the future. Present techniques of sleep learning have been only marginally successful, but with the means to induce information directly into the brain, who knows what may be possible. Again, it may be a matter of 'cracking the code'. Someday we will probably be able to play floppy discs directly into our brains. Hopefully, information won't take unless we are willing.

Hypnosis

Hypnosis does require a willing subject and it is another area which could be dramatically improved by applied magnetic fields. As it is now hypnosis is only about 20-30% effective. By magnetically driving the brain rhythms at certain frequencies it may be possible to induce a trance-like state such that a person would be extremely receptive to hypnosis. This could make it very helpful to anyone who wishes to improve sports abilities, transform habits, aid the healing process, improve learning skills, become more artistic, intuitive, psychic, etc. Research is already underway in this area.

Food Treatment

Since magnetic fields alter biochemistry, including enzyme activity and acid-base balance, they have great potential in the food industry. Perhaps each type of food will benefit from a specific type or polarity of magnetic field treatment depending on whether it needs ripening, sweetening, or preserving.

While the present methods of irradiation are suspect by many people, magnetic treatments may be much more socially acceptable and a lot more useful.

Magnetization of Other Materials

A special type of plastic has already been magnetized. In the future ways may be found to magnetize common substances such as wood, rocks, crystals, or ice. To magnetize such materials might require super strong fields which can be created with the use of super conductors. Such strong fields could align the nuclear spins of the atoms and then somehow "freeze" them to make them permanent. This could result in completely different applications of magnetism, difficult to foresee at this time. For example, experiments are already underway at the author's laboratory to electromagnetically tune crystals with the aim of making them more useful for helping the body rebalance.

Aging

This is definitely an area that will be important as knowledge of magnetic treatments increases in the future.   There are a number of reports about hair turning black, renewed sexual drive, etc., and older people who use PULSARS seem to greatly benefit from them.

Experiments with mice have already been done showing that increased lifespan is possible. One thing that happens when aging occurs is that the cells don't divide and grow as quickly, or when they do divide, each individual cell is not as healthy as the previous generation. In the case of cancer, cells divide and grow too rapidly. There is probably some relationship between the mechanisms that cause cancer and those that weaken cell growth, and when we learn how to eradicate cancer, we may learn things that will help stop the aging process.

Changing the Entire Planetary Field

We have electromagnetically polluted the planet. Radio waves of all frequencies blanket the Earth, relayed from mountain top to mountain top, bouncing back and forth between the ground and the conductive ionosphere, to and from satellites, and now even under the seas. Radio, radar, televison, and most especially, ordinary electric power lines, have significantly altered Earth's original electromagnetic quiet. Many of these radio and electromagnetic frequencies penetrate our homes as easily as light passes thru glass. At this time we don't know the full extent of harm we could be doing. Certainly not all frequencies and patterns are harmful—in fact some are even health producing or maintaining. However it has definitely been established that the ordinary 60 cycle electric power line fields are not healthy. Perhaps in the future we will correct the situation and use radio and power line frequencies that will be beneficial. Or perhaps at times of solar flares, which might be disturbing, we could temporarily alter the power grid of the entire planet to produce compensating fields. Such large scale changes could even alter the weather.

Interdimensional Travel

Going even farther into the future, we can imagine the possibility of changing the vibrational rate of the body so as to flip it into another dimension. This sounds like science fiction; but today's science fiction may become the science of the 21st century.

We tend to think that our universe is IT, the true, absolute, one and only reality, but this could simply be another of our ignorant egoisms. Evidence is increasing that parallel universes abound right here and now, interpenetrating or coexisting with this one. While we aren't usually aware of them, some people claim to perceive such universes, and a few have even traveled to them using certain mental gymnastics. Perhaps it is some magnetic orientation or vibrational frequency of our body's atomic nuclei that keeps us here, and not there, and by properly tuning ourselves with special instruments we could flip into an alternate universe. The first trips to elsewhere may be one-way, unless the traveler can send along the parts and supplies necessary to make an instrument for the trip back!

CHAPTER XI

SOURCES AND REFERENCES

MAGNETS, MAGNETIC INSTRUMENTS, AND DETECTORS

Permanent magnets can be obtained from industrial supply companies, hobby shops, and scientific supply houses. Magnets of many shapes and strengths can be ordered for most experimental purposes.

Bio Health Enterprises, Inc., P. 0. Box 628, Murray Hill, Kentucky 42071, sells a variety of permanent magnets, books, and other materials. Bio Health Enterprises offers a special monopolar magnet (one pole is shielded) so that muscle testing can be done with the energy of primarily only one pole.

Dowling Minor Magnetics Corporation., Box 1829, Sonoma, California 95476, offers three Biomagnetic kits. One kit is for initial work with magnets and living systems and consists of magnets of different shapes, sizes, and strengths. A second kit is for professional use and consists of different types of magnets, more sophisticated experiments, and one super strong Neodimium magnet and one very large, very strong, magnetic slab. Their third kit is a magnetic biofield meter which can be used to detect and measure the body's energy field.

Edwards Two, Ltd., 1530 Myrtle Ave., Monrovia, California 91016, manufactures little oval-shaped magnetic buttons called Magne-Tabs which are placed on the skin. Both poles are present to the body simultaneously.

Magna-Pak, P. O. Box 4264, Station C, London, Ontario, Canada N5W5J6, distributes a number of magnetic and electromagnetic devices. They offer a pulsed magnetic field instrument which has two independent applicators whose frequency can be varied from 1 to 1,000 hz. The price is $1,095 plus shipping.

Magnet & Halso, Box 239, 12725 Skarholmen, Stockholm, Sweden makes a full size pulsed magnetic field treatment system consisting of large coils which surround the body. It may not be possible to order these devices from overseas.

Mid-American Marketing, Box 124, Eaton, Ohio, 45320, markets a number of permanent magnet devices, such as bracelets, testing magnets, pads, necklaces, etc.

Oriental Medicine Supply, 1950 Washington St., Braintree, Mass 02130, carries acupuncture point magnets, magnetic belts, magnetic jewelry, books and other items.

PsychoPhysics Labs, Box 6023, Boulder, CO 80306, offers two types of pulsed magnetic field instruments - the **PULSAR** is a portable unit with rechargeable batteries, about the size of a tape cassette. A palm sized applicator produces a pulsing, polarized field of about 3 gauss, at a nominal frequency of 13 Hz. The **PULSAR** fits in a pocket or purse and can be effectively used for both diagnosis and treatment.

The **BIOPULSAR** is a professional research instrument which provides for two more applicators and functions. Frequency, waveform, and intensity can be independently varied. The BIOPULSAR can be used for electrotherapy treatments, either in the microamp or millamp range, for driving earphones or eye lights at brain wave frequencies, producing brain tuning currents and of course, magnetic applicators.

The **BIOPULSAR** is also a GSR biofeedback instrument and this function can be used simultaneously with the outputs to drive or alter the output frequencies. In other words, a person can be in a biological loop with the magnetic, audio, or photic output.

The **BIOPULSAR** can be used for experiments such as treating plants, driving magnetic coils for crystals, tuning individuals brainwaves to the same frequency, and so forth.

The company also offers a small magnetic pillow designed especially for low back pain. This convenient and inexpensive pillow is colored red for south polarity and blue for north, and can be used anywhere on the body. $50 + $3 shipping.

THE MAGNETIC SLEEPING SYSTEM is manufactured in Japan and distributed by PsychoPhysics Labs. Low strength magnets in the bed pad, deluxe down cover, and pillow provide magneto therapy while you sleep. Write or call Psycho-

Physics Labs to arrange a free demonstration in your area.

MAGNETIC HELMETS made of mu metal, a special and very expensive metal which provides magnetic and electric shielding, is also available from PsychoPhysics Labs. This is a custom made research device for experiments on meditation, brain wave research, etc. $700 + $25 shipping charge.

PSYCHOENERGETICS FITNESS DECK, a set of 52 photographically illustrated exercise cards designed to introduce variety into an exercise routine, is available from PsychoPhysics Labs for $19.95 + $1.75 shipping.

ANALYSIS OF PERSONAL RELATIONSHIPS. Lovers, parents and children, friends, or business partners can be much better understood by analysis of planetary patterns. Such an analysis can bring clarity to what seems confusing or disturbing, or conflictual. $25 per pair-from PsychoPhysics Labs.

See page 216 for additional sources and references.

BOOKS

Badgley, L. ENERGY MEDICINE, Human Energy Press, 370 West San Bruno Ave., San Bruno, Ca, 1987.

Bitter, F. MAGNETS—THE EDUCATION OF A PHYSICIST, Doubleday Anchor Books, Garden City, N. Y. 1959.

Becker, R. THE BODY ELECTRIC, W. Morrow, N. Y. 1985.

Bhattacharya, A. K. and Sierra, R. U. POWER IN A MAGNET TO HEAL. West Bengal, India, 1976.

Broeringmeyer, R. and M. ENERGY THERAPY, Bio Health Enterprises, Inc.,   P. 0. Box 628, Murray Hill, KY, 1989. $45.

Davis, A. R. and Rawls, W. C. THE MAGNETIC EFFECT, Exposition Press, Smithtown, N. Y., 1975.

Davis, A. R. and Rawls, W. C. MAGNETISM AND ITS EFFECT ON THE LIVING SYSTEM. Exposition Press, Hicksville, N. Y., 1974.

De la Warr, G.W. BIOMAGNETISM. Delawarr Laboratories, Ltd., Oxford, England . 1978

Eden, Jerome. ANIMAL MAGNETISM AND THE LIFE ENERGY. Exposition Press, Hicksville, NY. 1974

Gauquelin, M. THE COSMIC CLOCKS. Henry Regnery Co., Chicago, IL. 1967.

Herman, J.R. and Goldberg, R.A. SUN, WEATHER, AND CLIMATE, NASA, SP-426. 1978

Landscheidt, Theodor. SUN-EARTH-MAN: A MESH OF COSMIC OSCILLATIONS. Urania Trust, London, England. 1989

Mesmer, F.A. (Bloch, George, Ed). MESMER-ISM. William Kaufmann, Inc., Los Altos, CA. 1980

Payne, Buryl. BIOMEDITATION., AN INTE-GRATION OF BIOFEEDBACK, HYPNOSIS, AND MEDITATION. Available from PsychoPhysics Labs, $12.

Tenforde, T. S. MAGNETIC FIELD EFFECTS ON BIOLOGICAL SYSTEMS. Plenum, N.Y. N.Y.

PERIODICALS

BIO ENERGY HEALTH NEWSLETTER, published monthly by Bio Health Enterprises, P.O. Box 628, Murray Hill, KY 42701. $24 per year.

BEMI Currents, Newsletter of the Bio-Electro-Magnetics Institute, Dr. John Zimmerman, Editor, 165 Continental View Drive, Boulder, CO 80303. This informative, well written and delightfully illustrated newsletter will keep you informed of new items of interest, who's doing what, where, and how to participate. $12/year.

JOURNAL OF BIOELECTRICITY, Marcel Dekker, Inc. , 270 Madison Ave., New York, NY 10016. $62.50 per year.

MAGNETS IN YOUR FUTURE, P.O. Box 580, Temecula, CA 92390. This magazine reports on magnetic materials and sometimes includes articles on health and medicine. $25 per issue.

NATIONAL BUREAU OF STANDARDS, SOLAR GEOPHYSICAL DATA, Space Environment Services Center. 325 Broadway, Boulder, CO 80303. There is a $37 yearly charge for their weekly data report on sunspot numbers, planetary magnetic index and other technical information. They also have information available on magnetic tapes.

SOLAR AND PLANETARY INFLUENCES, A monthly newsletter providing forecasts of solar activity, geomagnetic activity, special weather patterns, and possible effects on human behavior. Each month a detailed analysis is also made of the previous predictions.   Sample newsletter for $4. Available from PsychoPhysics Labs,   848 Walnut Avenue, Santa Cruz, CA 95060.

ORGANIZATIONS

Academy for Peace Research, P.O. Box 697, Hanalei, HI 96714, publishes reports on The Global Meditation Project and other peace projects.

Bio Health Enterprises, Inc., P.O. Box 628, Murray, KY 42071, 1-800-626-3386, offers workshops, seminars and conferences on magnetism and health topics.

JOURNAL ARTICLES

Badgley, L. A New Method for Locating Acupuncture Points and Body Field Distortions. , Amer. Jo. of Acu. 12(3), 1984.

Bassett, A. L., Pulsing Electromagnetic Fields, A New Method to Modify Cell Behavior in Calcified and Noncalcified Tissue. Calcified Tissue Int. 34,1-8, 1982.

Becker, R. O. Relationship of Geomagnetic Environment to Human Biology. N. Y. State Jo. of Med., 2215 Aug. 1, 1983.

Bigg, E. K. Lunar and Planetary Influences on Geomagnetic Disturbances. Jo. of Geophysical Research, 68, 4099-5003, 1963.

Binder, A. Pulsed Electromagnetic Field Therapy of Persistent Rotator Cuff Tendinitis. The Lancet, Mar. 31, 1984.

Brown, F. A. et al. Magnetic Response of an Organism and It's Solar Relationships. Bio. Bull. 118 (3) 367-381, 1960.

Brown, F. A. & Chow, C. S. Interorganismic and Environmental Influence Through Extremely Weak Electromagnetic Fields. Bio. Bull., 144, 437-461, 1973.

Brown, F. A. & Chow, C. S. Non-equivalence for Bean Seeds of Clockwise and Counterclockwise Magnetic Motion: A Novel Terrestrial Adaptation? Bio. Bull. 148, 370-379, 1975.

Brown, F. & Chow, C. S. Differentiation Between Clockwise and Counterclockwise Magnetic Rotation by the Planarian, Dugesia Dorotacephala. Physio. Zoology, 48(2), 168-176, 1975.

Delgado, J., Magnetic Fields in Biology. Centro Ramon Y Cajal, Madrid, 34 Spain, 1984.

Dewey, E. R., Evidence of Cyclic Patterns in an Index of International War Battles, 600 B. C. - 1957 A. D. Cycles 21(6) 121-158, 1970.

Friedman, H. and Becker, R. O., Geomagnetic Parameters and Psychiatric Hospital Admissions. Nature, 200, 626-628, 1963.

Guseo, A. Pulsing Electromagnetic Field Therapy of Multiple Sclerosis by the Gyuling-Bordacs Device: Double-Blind, Cross-Over and Open Studies. Jo. Bioelec. 6(1), 23-35, 1987.

Gould, J. The Case for Magnetic Sensitivity in Bird And Bees. Am. Sci. 68(3) 256-267, 1980.

Harwood, J. M. and Malin, S. R. C. Sunspot Cycle Influence on the Geomagnetic Field. Geophysical Jo. of the Royal Ast. Soc., 50(3), 605-620, 1977.

Ito, H. and Bassett, A. L. Effect of Weak, Pulsing, Electromagnetic Fields on Neural Regeneration in the Rat. Clin. Orthopaedics and Related Res. 283-290, 1983.

Lau, B. Effects of Low Frequency Electromagnetic Field on Blood Circulation: Treatment of Sports Injuries and Osteoarthritis. Unpublished, but available from: Dept. of Microbiology, Loma Linda University, Loma Linda, CA.

Laloe, F. and Freed, J., The Effects of Spin in Gases. Scientific American, April, 94-101, 1988.

Murayama, M. Orientation of Sickled Erythrocyctes in a Magnetic Field. Nature, 206(420), 1965.

Nelson, J. H. Short Wave Radio Propagation; Correlation with Planetary Positions. RCA Review, 26-34, March, 1951.

Papatheofanis, F. J. et al., Applied Static Magnetic Field Induction of Bone Mineralization In Vivo. College of Medicine, Dept. of Orthopaedics, Univ. of Ill, Chicago, Ill. 60612.

Pautrizel, R. et al., Stimulation Of Protection Mechanisms by Magnetic Fields and Electromagnetic Waves (Priore Apparatus). Laboratoire d'Immunologie et de Biologie Parasitaire, Universite Bordeaux II, 146 Rue Leo Saignat, 33076 Bordeaux, Cedex, France.

Payne, B. A New Device Which Detects and Measures an Energy Field Around the Human Body. Am. Jo. of Acupuncture, 11(4), 1983.

Payne, B. Polarity Shifts in a Human Biofield At Times of a New and Full Moon. Geocosmic News, 4, 1983.

Payne, B. Cycles of Peace, Sunspots, and Geomagnetic Activity. Cycles, May, 1984.

Payne, B. Magnetism and Medical Astrology. National Council for Geocosmic Research, 4(2) 5-6, 1986.

Payne, B. Global Peace Meditation Research Project. National Council for Geocosmic Research 5(3) 1987.

Prince, J. P. The Use of Low Strength Magnets on EAV Points Am. Jo. of Acu. 11(2) 125-130, 1983.

Ross, C. An Instrument Which is Set in Motion by Vision or Proximity of The Human Body. Lancet, 222, July 30, 1922.

Shan, Lian-Lian, Magnetic Acupoint Therapy for Treatment of Neurasthenia. Am. Jo. of Acu. 14(1) 51-53, 1986.

Surgalla, L. A. Molecular Mechanisms of Magnetic Medicine. Magnets in Your Future, 3(4) April, 1988.

Surgalla, L. A. Effect of Weak Pulsed Extremely Low Frequency Electromagnetic Fields on Rate of Transport in Isolated Sarcoplasmic Reticulum. Integrity Electronics and Research, Inc. Buffalo, N. Y.

Warnke, U. Infrared Radiation And Oxygen Partial Pressure in Human Tissue as Indicators of The Therapeutic Effects of Pulsating Magnetic Fields. University of Saarbrucken, Veriagsgesellschaft fur Biophysik und Medizin, Sperberweg 2, 6200, Wiesbaden, West Germany

Wood, K. D. Sunspots and Planets. Nature, 240, Nov. 10, 1972.

About The Author

Buryl Payne graduated Magna Cum Laude, Phi Beta Kappa, from the University of Washington. He holds a Ph. D. in Psychology and an M. S. in Physics. While a graduate student he designed, developed, and marketed the first commercial biofeedback instruments. He holds a patent on the GSR type of biofeedback instrument sold by Radio Shack and Thought Technology. He founded the company now known as PsychoPhysics Labs. He was on the faculties of Goddard College in Vermont and Boston University prior to directing a holistic health clinic in Boston called The Institute for PsychoEnergetics. Upon the invitation of Dr. Ralph Sierra, he studied at the Biomagnetics Research Laboratory in Puerto Rico in 1974, about the time he discovered the device which measures the Biofield. He has discovered three other energy field effects not heretofore known to classical science, written two books on consciousness and many papers on a wide range of scientific subjects. He is currently designing and researching new magnetic field devices, as well as teaching dance and movement, and yoga.

ELECTRONIC MAGNETIC BED
Coils in a bed produce pulsed magnetic fields varying from 1 to 30 Hz, with different wave forms. For experimental use only. Custom specifications possible.

NIKKEN MAGNETIC PRODUCTS and other magnets, magnetic devices, and unique instruments are available from the **BodyMind Connection**, 1108 Spruce Street, Boulder, CO 80302 (303) 443-7029.